MW01068208

A Question of Values

PAUL L. ERRINGTON

A Question of Values

Edited by Carolyn Errington

 *IOWA STATE UNIVERSITY PRESS, AMES*

To Frederick and Frances Hamerstrom

PAUL L. ERRINGTON was internationally recognized for his work in the population phenomena of vertebrates, especially fur and game species, and made extensive studies in this field in North America and Northern Europe. Dr. Errington was professor of zoology at Iowa State University before his death in 1962. He became a staff member at Iowa State in 1932, the same year he received his doctorate from the University of Wisconsin. Recipient of many awards, he was given the American Wildlife Conference Aldo Leopold Medal (1962), a yearly award in recognition of the highest achievement and service to wildlife conservation. He was twice honored by the Wildlife Society for outstanding wildlife publication.

In 1958–1959 Professor Errington conducted research in Europe on population dynamics of higher vertebrates with the support of the Guggenheim and National Science foundations and the Swedish government.

He was a fellow of the American Association for the Advancement of Science and the American Ornithologists Union and member of the Society of Zoologists and numerous other scientific organizations.

© 1987 Iowa State University Press, Ames, Iowa 50010
All rights reserved
Composed by Iowa State University Press
Printed in the United States of America

First edition, 1987

Library of Congress Cataloging-in-Publication Data

Errington, Paul Lester.
　A question of values.

　Includes index.
　　1. Nature conservation—United States.　2. Nature conservation—Canada.　3. Zoology—United States.　5. Errington, Paul Lester.
I. Errington, Carolyn.　II. Title.
QH76.E77　　1987　　333.95′16′0973　　87–16978
ISBN 0-8138-1444-8

FRONTISPIECE: PAUL ERRINGTON RECORDED WHAT HAPPENED WITHIN A FREE-LIVING MUSKRAT POPULATION
Photo, Marion Ferguson

CONTENTS

INTRODUCTION

PAUL ERRINGTON'S preface to Of Men and Marshes *and his preface to* The Red Gods Call *that follow substitute for the more usual biographical introduction. These two prefaces go a long way toward answering the question: Who was Paul Errington?*

PREFACE TO *Of Men and Marshes*

M Y own experience with glacial marshes started with muddy feet on the family farm in east-central South Dakota. It continued through years of hunting and fur trapping and through the long-term research programs that accompanied and followed my rather erratic evolution from a professional trapper to a biologist and college professor.

I have seen and lived among the plains and mountains of the West and the coniferous forests and open lakes of the North, and I know some of the great scenic areas of our continent. These I love, too, yet for me as an individual, no other natural feature has ever had the enduring attraction of an undespoiled chain of marshes in an undespoiled setting of glacial hills.

Feeling as I do, it is hard for me to understand the willingness of the public to drain marshes even if the land so drained might produce corn or some other profitable agricultural crop. Monetary profit should not be the sole objective for land use. We need cornfields and economic bases for our civilization, but we also need marshes where they may be said to belong.

The wise ancients, in writing that man does not live by bread alone, doubtless had in mind something similar to what I have, though I do not know that they valued marshes as part of their cultural surroundings. Very possibly they did not, and they may have had reasons not to, for some marshes have meant big problems at some times for some peoples. At any rate, the ancients recognized that there should be more in human experience than making a living.

I believe that marshes could add greatly to human enjoyment if more people really knew them the year around. I believe that there would be more interest in marshes if more people appreciated how interesting and beautiful marshes are as marshes. Greater familiarity with marshes on the part of more people could give man a truer and a more wholesome view of himself in relation to Nature. In marshes, life's undercurrents and unknowns and evolutionary changes are exemplified with a high degree of independence from human dominance as long as the marshes remain in marshy condition. Marshes comprise their own form of wilderness. They have their own life-rich genuineness and reflect forces that are much older, much more permanent, and much mightier than man.

PREFACE TO *The Red Gods Call*

I first saw reference to the Red Gods and their calling during my high school youth. I did not see it first in Kipling's poem about the restless feet of young men who wanted to be up and away because the Red Gods called. Rather, I think that it was in the caption for a now-forgotten picture. The picture undoubtedly featured something wonderfully exciting for a youngster who loved the out-of-doors and manly adventure; but I no longer remember whether it was of autumn haze and autumn colors, of duck hunting with rain or snow in the air, of a canoe in choppy water, of northland winter, or of something else. It does not matter that the picture seems always to be changing in my memory, that I no longer have any idea how much or how little the recollections coming to my mind may have originated with any picture. So far as the keenness of my responses are concerned and my longing to answer the Red Gods and to be up and away, it does not matter at all.

By my earliest teens I was hunting, fishing, trapping, camping, and prowling about the out-of-doors in Brookings County, east-central South Dakota. As my apprenticeship for a naturalist's career progressed, I carried on my outdoor activities more and more professionally. When I became aware of the Red Gods as so designated, I was already "living off the country" as a fur trapper to the extent that this could be made to fit in with school and day-labor jobs. The Red Gods did not start anything in my case; they merely afforded a sort of recognition, emphasizing in my consciousness what I loved so much and reminding me that what I loved must also be loved by many other people.

All together my early fur-trapping experience covered a period of thirteen winters, 1915–1928, including the initial "kid trapping" in home neighborhoods. After I finished high school in 1920, the fur trapping contributed very substantially to or made up the chief source of my livelihood almost to the beginning of my graduate training in 1929. Small-time though my trapping was compared to some professional trapping, it virtually put me through South Dakota State College. Most of my trapping then was centered about the family farm in the Oakwood-Tetonkaha lake and marsh chain west of Bruce and along the Big Sioux River west of Brookings; but I also spent one winter trapping along the Cheyenne River and its drainage in Haakon County of western South Dakota and another in northern Minnesota's Big Bog, Beltrami, and Koochiching counties.

From graduate training on through thirty years on the faculty of Iowa State College, now Iowa State University, I worked with much the same types of animal life, the same types of geographic terrain, and the same types of outdoor values that so fascinated me as a trapper. I went on biological expeditions over the American Northwest and the Scandinavian Arctic and Subarctic; my memories of these are of tents and patrol cabins, of canoes and pack trails, of overloaded automobiles, of wildlife refuges and fur preserves. I am glad to say that I have been able to spend a large part of my life where wild things lived in freedom in northern scenes where they belonged—the minks, otters, and muskrats; the ducks, grouse, quail, and birds of prey; the foxes, coyotes, and wolves.

When it comes to responding to what is clean and wild and free, I know I have heard the Red Gods calling. I have heard them in classroom, laboratory, and library, and in surroundings remote from untampered nature; I have heard them despite mosquito and blackfly bites, despite hunger and fatigue and worries. I have heard the Red Gods all of my life.

RESEARCH ON AN IOWA MARSH IN SUMMER
REQUIRED PHYSICAL ENDURANCE.

I

OF PREDATION

WHEN PAUL ERRINGTON BEGAN GRADUATE study at the University of Wisconsin in 1929, it was generally supposed that predation—the killing of one animal by another—determined to a large extent the population level of a prey species. It followed that hunters would have available to them a greater abundance of quail, pheasants, rabbits—or whatever else it was they wanted to hunt during the hunting season—if hawks, owls, foxes—or whatever else preyed upon them—were eliminated.

Paul set out to test the validity of this supposition. The question "What does really count in determining numbers of a free-living animal population?" fascinated him. It was the question, above all other unanswered questions in his field of vertebrate ecology, he wanted to answer. And it was the question he did answer during his many years of professional study.

As data accumulated and as conclusions were justified, his research results were published in an extensive body of technical papers, bulletins and books, and in nontechnical writ-

PREDATION IN NATURE IS A WAY OF LIFE,
NOT TO BE JUDGED AS GOOD OR EVIL.

ings such as those reprinted in Part I of this collection of essays.

The three articles that follow were all published in Audubon Magazine: *"A Closer Look at the Killers" in 1953, "The 'Big Boss' of the Woods" in 1954, and "Our Little Wild Dogs: The Foxes" in 1955.*

A Closer Look at the Killers

I N DESERT OR OCEAN DEPTH, ON MOUNTAIN TOP or steppe or fertile prairie, in lake or stream or marsh or forest or cave, life follows patterns of encroachment and adjustment that certainly were established in their broader outlines long before man was present to concern himself about them. Apart from the refinements evolved by man, life is mainly a process of unimaginative exploitation of the exploitable, with the participants living as they can.

The known details of this exploitation are so varied as to discourage generalizing, and I shall not try too hard to do so. Rather, I shall write of those animals we call predators. I shall write of them not only because of the many years of my own professional studies that have been devoted to them but also because of the durable misconceptions of predation that still carry over in public thought.

It is unfortunate that man, the specialist in evil, sees in predation among wild animals so much evil that isn't there. Predation as a phenomenon is as nearly worldwide as any way of life followed by organisms. It is the only way of life many, many animals—from microscopic protozoa up to the great whales—are adapted to follow at all. It fits naturally into the old, old patterns of life being maintained somehow, when, and where, it can be.

The moth larva that bores through an apple isn't doing anything so much different from what a wasp larva may do in the body of a caterpillar or what a robber fly does when it pokes its mouth parts into a grasshopper. The reindeer browsing on the tundra doesn't succumb to temptation when it eats the eggs in a duck nest—it is just eating. The raccoon eating fallen plums has no reason to think that it shouldn't eat the newborn litter of rabbits that it may find at the same time—or dig crayfishes out

Audubon Magazine 55(1):12–15, 22, 23 (1953).

of their holes or pursue a crippled bird that doesn't want to be caught.

We may have turkeys feeding upon large insects—and also upon small snakes if they can catch them, or possibly upon the eggs and fledglings of small birds. Or the predation may be highly specialized, a species of predator living exclusively upon one species of prey. The Everglade kite has a beak enabling it to extract a particular kind of large snail from its shell. The goshawk has some specialization in its short, rounded wings by which it can "sprint-fly" through brush in pursuit of a dodging bird, but it also can and does prey upon mammals. Unlike the goshawk, the peregrine falcon is adapted for swift and sustained pursuit through open air and seldom, if ever, catches its prey in brush or on the ground. The great horned owl is a very general feeder upon nearly everything catchable from insects and spiders to skunks and geese, yet no one examining its soft flight feathers would call it an unspecialized bird. Likewise, the wonderfully keen noses of members of the weasel and dog families may be considered a real specialization for their way of living, irrespective of how general their food habits may be.

In considering predation as a phenomenon, it should not be forgotten that the animals pursued or preyed upon have adaptations, as well, and that many of those suffering the heaviest predation have lived with their predators for some millions of years—and not solely because of their own high breeding rates. Wild animal predators are by no means always able to take their prey exactly as they may wish. Except for the most special of special cases, the records from careful investigations have brought out over and over again that the one big thing that determines what shall be preyed upon is *availability.* Nature shows scant favoritism in dealing with her creatures. The exploitable is exploited by about whatever can do it.

For extremely abundant small forms—teeming populations of insects or fishes, sometimes of mice, lemmings, rabbits, and so on—availability may mean their local, or regional, abundance. As long as these great abundances prevail, practically all animals having appetites and the ability to capture these "prey animals" can take them virtually at will. Upon the larger or less numerous animal life, predation may or may not be so closely dependent upon abundance, but it is still linked with availability of prey.

We can recognize, of course, that animal life feeds upon

something or it doesn't keep on living, and if that "something" is not plants, it has to be animals. But what about the sorts of predation that come close enough to us personally to arouse questions as to whether we should intervene, and, if so, how much?

If we live in town, we may know that the owl-roosts in the pine or cedar grove have bird remains under them and that those remains include more than the unwanted starlings and house sparrows. A sharp-shinned or small Cooper's hawk may wrestle all over someone's lawn with a flicker that is almost too strong for it to manage, and then the hawk may sit there with outspread wings, taking bites out of the struggling victim. A squirrel may be seen carrying away something fluffy that is *not* an acorn, or a bull snake with bulges along its sides may lie under the bushes while the neighborhood birds flutter around it, or our pet chickadee may no longer show up at the suet, or there may be piles of feathers that we can't fully account for but we suspect. . . .

If we live in the country, we may note that a red-tailed hawk is interested in our poultry yard, and we need not delude ourselves that it is after a rat if it can get its meat hooks into one of those expensive fries. There may be raccoon or opossum or skunk tracks in the dust behind the coops. There may be a covey of nine bobwhites coming to the buildings during a late January snow and only five when next we see them. Something predatory may be visiting the mourning dove nests in the grove, or we may see a snapping turtle feeding on a duck down at the pond, or the grouse or pheasants or rabbits or squirrels may never become anywhere nearly as numerous as we may think they should.

A distinction should be made before we go further: domesticated species can be so inept about protecting themselves or escaping predators that predation upon them falls in a very different category from predation upon the usual run of nature-tested wild mammals and birds. The poultryman has as much real cause as anyone to worry about losses he may suffer from predation, but even he may often greatly reduce his losses without much if any direct campaigning against the predators. Perhaps this may be accomplished through intelligent selection of a location or through improvement of housing, perhaps through something as simple as keeping an active dog to scare away foxes or providing shelters for chickens to run under if attacked by hawks. An enlightened game breeder I know, whose pheasant pens were being raided by eagles he was most reluctant to kill, stung the eagles with small shot at long range until they learned to stay away.

A tremendous amount of field research has been done on a number of North American wild mammals and birds. The resulting literature has brought out substantial evidence that looks incompatible with several of the earlier concepts of predation as a factor limiting populations of prey species. I shall not undertake the impossible task of discussing the newer evidence thoroughly or critically in a short article, but I should outline visible trends.

A major difference between predation in which one animal limits the population of another by preying upon it, and predation that is centered upon a population surplus, may be pointed up by an analogy. If cats, dogs, chickens, pigs, or rats drank the milk within a milk pail or contaminated it, such would have a quite different significance in dairy production than if they merely cleaned up milk spilled on the ground from a full pail. These are about the differences we find in studying the effects of predation on animal populations in nature. Some predation *can* cut into populations, with the net result of there being fewer prey animals maintaining themselves. This may be conspicuously the case when the predator is an enterprising exotic, or introduced animal, with which its prey lacks experience. On the other hand, a surprising amount of predation upon our favorite game species or songbirds is upon "spilled milk," which has no real chance of being other than wastage, whether it is eaten by flesh eaters or not.

For at least those common mammals and birds that have definite ideas as to property rights and the degree of crowding that they will put up with, their populations and rates of annual increase may be more or less self-limited. The fights between robins on the lawn, much of the singing or calling of birds during their breeding season, the pulling off of coveys of quail by themselves, and the many demonstrations of intolerance on the part of this or that species can all signify with varying degrees of emphasis something that, as realists, we should try to remember: *Essentially, there is room only for about so many of what the animal behaviorists call a "territorial species," in a particular area, at a particular time.*

The "threshold of security," or supporting capacity of an

area for a territorial species, should properly be thought of in a relative sense. Its values, expressed numerically, may differ with the year, and with the time of year, and, in addition, with the state of the environment. For our long-studied bobwhites, grouse, pheasants, and muskrats of the north central states, threshold values, or supporting capacity of environments, have seemed to be generally lowest during or near the years ending in sixes and sevens, and highest during or near the years ending in ones and twos. Just what is behind these and many other "cyclic" manifestations we do not know. During a given year threshold values tend to be highest in late summer or early fall, after the breeding season is over; lowest in spring, with the onset of a new breeding season and its new tensions; and intermediate in winter, when the habitat is neither so comparatively unrestricted as in late summer and early fall, nor so full of assertive competitors, as in spring.

There are deadly climatic emergencies—sweeping die-offs, and the like—but the factors that genuinely govern populations may still operate with a good deal of constancy. The "ceilings" of individual bobwhites or muskrats to be accommodated in an area may remain very similar for years at a stretch, and the year-to-year population responses may then follow mathematical patterns. Especially informative is the frequency with which a prey population may increase in conformity to a definite curve, with little or no deviation that can logically be attributed to variations in kinds and numbers of predatory enemies nor to actual predator pressures upon the prey. These instances illustrate the fundamental independence that many prey species may show toward predation as a limiting factor, even when the predation may account for colossal numbers of individuals or of large proportions of the prey populations.

Almost anyone who carries on intensive life-history observations of common mammals and birds may find them preyed upon, sometimes quite severely at immature stages. As I saw my litters of muskrats, marked for later identification, or broods of quail or pheasants or ducklings shrinking away, and at the same time saw their remains at the feeding places and in the droppings and pellets of local predators, I could understand the despair people might feel while witnessing losses suffered by species in which they had special interests.

But whether anything is done to give the species preyed upon added protection or not, I see no justification for the emotional intemperance that one creature, killing another, often arouses in people. After all, the broods of small to medium-sized hawks and owls that I have worked with shrank away in a similar manner. Why is it so widely believed that predators do not have their own losses from predation? In fact, I do not know of anything that suffers more downright severe "natural" killing, or predation, in relation to their numbers than do weasels. Still if weasel numbers are controlled by this predation, it would seem to be mainly in the poorer environment for weasels. In their better environment, weasel numbers appear to be determined more by the limits that weasels tolerate among themselves than by what may or may not prey upon them.

In analysis, predation upon most well-studied species of wild mammals and birds is borne notably by parts of populations that try to live under a handicap. If discovered by a predator, an unguarded clutch of eggs or a helpless litter is more vulnerable than the young that can scamper off and hide, and the less advanced young are more vulnerable than the strong fliers and runners or the ones that can fight back. Predation upon such ailing, weakened, or crippled individuals as we may loosely term "the unfit" does occur, but most of the thousands of victims of predation I have handled had the appearance of being physically normal for their ages. One who looks for obvious physical handicaps in the animals preyed upon may expect to find them only now and then. Exceptions may be those prey species that happen to be all but immune to predation. Even so, among these—the very young, the very old, the very ill, or the very unlucky, may not escape predation.

Handicaps imposed by circumstances may so often underlie availability to predators that it may be hard to find examples of victims that clearly were *not* members of biological surpluses or of parts of populations evicted by poor environments or environments already filled to capacity with their own kind, or otherwise made vulnerable by emergencies. When there is, in effect, a place for only about so many individuals of a species to live—for reasons of either or both environmental limitations or psychological peculiarities of the species—and when more than that number try to live there, tragic events have ways of befalling the excess populations.

In animals as dissimilar as bobwhites and muskrats, predation may be invited by overflows of populations into unfavorable habitat or by increased tension and friction in the social structure, even of individuals occupying the best habitats. Remains of the dead and "sign" of wholesale murders may be scattered about the landscape for a time. But, after Nature's period of shaking down to comfortable or manageable population limits is over, both the bobwhites and the muskrats may live with remarkable security for months, even in the presence of large numbers of such formidable predators as horned owls in bobwhite range and minks in muskrat range.

With increasing knowledge of these natural interplays, one can hardly avoid being impressed by the automatic ways in which they work—always within the rules of order imposed by protoplasm and its environment. Common predators switch from one type of prey to another, in keeping with the outstanding role of availability which determines their food habits. Common prey animals, in their turn, show many types of population counterbalancing.

If predation by minks upon muskrats or by horned owls upon bobwhites is heavy, losses from other enemies tend to diminish in proportion; in the absence of the minks or the horned owls, losses from other animals preying upon muskrats or bobwhites tend to increase. The muskrats, themselves, can be the greatest killers of other muskrats in places lacking their typical predatory enemies. And if losses of early born young are unusually severe, there may be, in compensation, not only prolonged late breeding but also high rates of survival of the late born young. Conversely, if losses of early born young are unusually light, the season's breeding may not only cease early but the loss rates of the late born may also be exceedingly high, and so on.

While it doesn't always happen that all loss from predation or from any other cause of death to prey animals is wholly compensated, at any one time or ever, far more natural compensating occurs than people are in the habit of thinking. That is the supreme reason why so many prey species may thrive despite our misgivings or our expressed wonder that they can exist at all under the pressure put upon them by predators.

Instead of taking it for granted that the eating of an egg or the killing of a young animal by a predator must mean one less of the prey species to be around by the opening of the hunting season or one less for the next year or the like, we should keep in mind that such loss from predation *may* be chiefly a *symptom* and only *incidental* to some of the things that *really dominate* populations.

To me, the great fascination of animal predation as a subject for study has lain in its varied manifestations of the timeless laws of life. Predators are among those wild creatures that maintain their integrity as wild creatures regardless of human meddling and man's ridiculous propensity for judging wildlife as good or bad according to moral standards of his own invention that he hardly pretends to adhere to, himself. Many predators are surely among the wildest and freest of all creatures. Of our native wildlife, the predators, too, include some of the rarest, the most beautiful, and the most superbly adapted animals. To some of us, they offer highly regarded antidotes to the banalities of a civilization top heavy with people.

I do not maintain that it may never be necessary to protect our economic or other interests from predators of one kind or another. Let us do whatever needs to be done in this respect, but, in so doing, let us weigh values and avoid senseless extremes.

The "Big Boss" of the Woods

N MY MORE MATURE YEARS, I HAVE COME TO dislike having a wild creature referred to as stupid because its learning capacity is patently subhuman. Mentally gifted man need not use the word so freely, with at least a faint implication that something is wrong with owls, turtles, frogs, fishes, worms, and essentially the rest of the animal kingdom for not being as smart as he is.

The "smart" crow may be plenty stymied when up against something for which its own behavior patterns do not suffice. The red fox, that traditional embodiment of subhuman cleverness, may not have to go so far beyond its everyday experiences to act in ways that could be called stupid. For all of the rigidities in its behavior, our horned owl lives with a matter-of-fact practicality that may still be sufficient for it at most times; the species may still be rated as biologically successful over large regions of the world, even in some that are thickly settled by inimical man.

Broadly, its behavior patterns must have been established millions of years ago. North American horned owls that are subject to human persecution may become exceedingly wary—slipping out of one side of a grove as a person approaches the opposite side or staying safe distances from firearms—or individual owls may pick out places where the hunting is good or make some other adjustments. It is with respect to modifying behavior in radical ways that the owls do not seem to have what it takes. When beset by a novel emergency, the horned owl is likely to meet it in the old, old way or not at all.

Within limits, the horned owl can take care of itself individually—that is, a well-situated, fully grown bird usually can. Somewhere over its range, an individual may die of disease, from grappling a porcupine, or by the talons of a goshawk, a big

Audubon Magazine 56(3):124–27 (1954).

13

falcon, or an eagle. I suspect that one of these owls could get badly ripped up by tackling prey with the teeth, durability, and disposition of a mink, house cat, or raccoon. A bird having the horned owl's weight and capabilities of swift flight could have an accident breaking a wing or impaling its body on a sharp point. The annual surpluses of horned owl young may find themselves involved in a great variety of troubles while wandering about the countryside. Any horned owl, young or old, secure living or otherwise, may have to submit to daytime harassing by other birds—especially by the crows and jays that seem to enjoy pestering them, and by some of the hawks that may attack horned owls in fury. But the horned owl's natural endowments are those of a most formidable bird of prey that can take punishment if it has to. It may not have the toughness of a snapping turtle, but the horned owl, too, is with us today after millions of years partly because it is tough.

Responsiveness of the parent owls to human intrusion varies from keeping out of sight to the most ferocious defense. An attack by a horned owl defending its young can be dangerous to a person who doesn't know what to expect. A few horned owl parents put on an injury-feigning act, similar to those of the innumerable smaller birds that so behave when an intruder comes too close to a nest or to helpless young. The most outstanding display that I ever saw came as the culmination of much hooting, beak-snapping, diving at my head, and miscellaneous frenzied antics in behalf of a fledgling that had jumped out of the nest at my approach without being quite able to keep on in level flight. This was one of the most amusing sights that I ever saw—that huge parent owl bouncing along on the forest floor with wings dragging. The significance of the injury feigning was not that the owl tried to look invitingly helpless and delectable, nor tried to imitate anything, nor that injury feigning must have useful purpose in the life of the species. A more logical explanation would be that the horned owl has the ancient behavior patterns of birds rather generally and that a reaction to one of these ancient patterns was touched off by the stresses of the occasion.

The horned owl is not much of a nest builder and, in most places with which I am familiar, it lays its eggs in tree cavities or in hawk or crow nests of previous years. A common procedure is for a pair of the owls to select, anywhere from fall to late winter, territorial headquarters in the vicinity of a strong nest of

14

a red-tailed hawk wherein to lay their eggs in February. Other nesting sites are ledges or crevices in rocky bluffs. I have found horned owls nesting on the ground in western South Dakota, sheltered only by low, brushy vegetation. It is not surprising to learn of nesting sites in undisturbed man-made structures, in a tower or church steeple or isolated building. Squirrel nests may be used where better nesting sites are lacking, although they may be so flimsy that they fall apart with eggs or owlets in them.

Two or three eggs comprise a normal set for horned owls to lay in Wisconsin and Iowa. After a month of incubation, the owl chick is out of its shell, looking anything but sturdy against the setting of blizzardy subzero weather that March often brings. If the first nesting attempt fails definitely enough for the mother owl to recognize failure, a second clutch may be laid, perhaps with a single egg. As a rule, adult horned owls take good care of their young, their solicitude increasing as the owlets grow to free-flying stages.

The young usually leave the nest five or six weeks after hatching and are fed by the parent birds for about three months more, or into July and August. "Mooching" from the more tolerant parents may continue into fall, but, at last, the old birds, having had all they want of their season's young, fly from tree to tree to get away from them, beak snapping as they go. Or they may inflict punishment on the young that hurts. And the cries of the young—denoting begging, hunger, or just plain habit or inclination to call—may be heard in the daytime as well as at night. This means that one or two or three more juvenile horned owls may be "weaned" and on their own, not necessarily enjoying their full independence and the catching of grasshoppers and garter snakes, but learning to live somehow. Where they go and what they do from then on is up to them, within the restrictions imposed by other owls and by the rest of the world.

There are in "territorial" forms of life, including the horned owl, certain intolerances that operate as natural population controls. Topnotch environment harbors a maximum of about so many "property-conscious" individuals at a given time—the number so tolerated by the species in question—but these individuals typically get along pretty well and serve as a more or less secure breeding nucleus. This is true to a lesser extent in the less choice environment, but, in these, more variation in

15

populations and breeding success may be noted. The annual overflow, or surplus production, from the functional breeding territories of an area tends to be frittered away in time if no additional environment can accommodate it.

For a species such as the horned owl, which *can* live twenty to thirty years, relatively few of the young raised during a breeding season might really be needed as replacements. Traps and guns account for a large share of the horned owl surpluses in northern United States, but the assumption should not be made that tremendously increased horned owl populations would result if human intervention would cease.

Some of my central Iowa study areas have had remarkably stable horned owl populations during the more than two decades that I have worked on them. Their "saturation densities" for the breeding months have been approximately a pair of adults per two square miles, together with similar numbers of nesting red-tailed hawks. Horned owls are shot by most farmers and hunters having opportunities, but the intensity of human persecution varies from place to place and from year to year. The warier owls are adept at preventing themselves from being shot, and if a member of a pair is killed, the survivor doesn't seem to have much difficulty in getting a new mate before so very long.

Much drifting about of juvenile owls goes on in fall and early winter, which drifting may temporarily increase the local horned owl populations above the late winter average of one per mile. On quiet November evenings one may hear their hooting from several directions at once, yet in the process of challenging and counterchallenging, age-sanctioned rights ultimately prevail, and the woods are left to the owls that "own" them, to those staying to breed.

The poorer grades of horned owl environment may be those where any owl may be visible for long distances in straggling timber, those where farm groves may be dangerously close to people who do not want horned owls near, or where otherwise a place may not offer all that horned owls need for continued existence. They may either offer a precarious living for any of the birds or be perfectly suitable except for reproduction.

An example of the second type of marginal habitat is furnished by a small wooded island in a marsh. The island has been occupied for at least the past nine years by a pair of horned owls (possibly not always by the same owls) having access to an

16

abundance of food. Almost every year the island owls were known to have made a nesting attempt, which regularly failed for the apparent reason that owls had nothing better than squirrels' nests in which to lay their eggs. At the same time the continued presence of horned owls on such a small island could well be the explanation for red-tailed hawks or crows not building their more substantial nests there.

Thus we see how even a species we may think of as a "big boss" among wild creatures, even when individuals live securely in food-rich places, cannot expand its effective breeding range beyond that which the environment permits.

Food may or may not be a limiting factor in the horned owl's life. I can understand how its food resources could be critically short in a snow-covered wilderness during a "cyclic low" of snowshoe hares. The owls can starve or engage in mass movements away from foodless regions. I can readily understand also how badly eroded farmlands, deserts, and other such places, might not have sufficient food to support *many* horned owls. Conversely, situations may be very different in rich agricultural country, where the rodents, rabbits, large insects, and other wildlife often may be far more than plentiful enough to support all the predators that the predators themselves may tolerate.

From the studies of food habits of horned owls and eagle owls that have been conducted in North America and Europe, respectively, we may conclude that the owls show little of what could be termed food preferences as long as their prey is neither too small nor too large. The smaller prey such as late summer grasshoppers and crickets are taken both by the juveniles that cannot catch much else and by old birds responding to seasonal availability of a food supply. May beetles, carrion beetles, and crayfishes may frequently be fed upon, and occasionally an owl pellet (casting) may be made up of heads and skins of cutworms. Eight of one lot of thirteen horned owl pellets from a dry creek in western South Dakota contained remains totaling sixty-seven individuals of the wolf spider, *Lycosa*.

Cold-blooded vertebrates taken are usually garter snakes, frogs, and tiger salamanders, the latter of which may overrun some areas for brief periods in spring and fall. Fishes may be preyed upon when circumstances make them available to owls.

Staple prey consists of the commoner and most available mammals and birds—notably cottontails and snowshoe hares, field-living barn rats, mice of many species, shrews, almost any-thing within manageable size limits that happens to be conspic-uous and easy to lay claws on. Poorly housed domestic chick-ens are easy prey for horned owls. At times, the owls may depend heavily upon pocket gophers and moles, flickers, pheasants, quail, grouse, grebes, rails, coots, ducks, weasels, domestic pigeons, small owls, muskrats, flying squirrels, black-birds, sparrows, and shorebirds.

The one dietary rule of the horned owl that holds through-out regularities and irregularities alike, is that *prey is taken much in order of its availability in places where horned owls are in the habit of hunting.* Differences in availability of prey to predators may be difficult to unravel in analyses of complicated predator-prey relationships, but in the best-understood cases that have been studied for mammals and birds, they boil down mainly to differences in numbers of prey animals that are hav-ing trouble with their own kinds or with their environments.

Populations overflow from good environment into poor. Parts of animal populations beset by friction with animal neighbors, parts of populations finding themselves in a bad way because of fires, droughts, floods, deep snows, overgrazing by livestock, destruction of food or cover by man, and an endless array of other big or little crises—these exemplify the things that increase availability of prey for the horned owls. On the other hand, a quail population wintering comfortably may suf-fer little or no predation from horned owls hunting over it every night. Or horned owls may hunt for months next to a lush cat-tail marsh having thousands of thriving muskrats without catching *any* of them. Even the cottontail, which at population levels commonly found in the northern states is as consistently vulnerable to horned owl predation as any native species I could mention, may live with comparative security from the owls if it has the advantage of strong environment that is not too full of its own kind. Overproduced or insecure wildlife tends to get "shaken down to fit" the environment somehow, whether through the agency of horned owl predation or something else.

The studies of predator-prey relationships that have long been in progress in our north-central region indicate that the public there becomes far too easily excited about the harm that the horned owl does or is believed to do. Partly, this is due to misconceptions not only as to what the owl does in its hunting and feeding but also as to what kind of bird it is and how it lives.

An enlightened society no longer regards owls as the creatures of evil that the ancients did, to be identified with malignant spirits, harbingers of death, and so on, but many unrealistic views have carried over into modern life. Reputable bird students have been among those who have outdone themselves in applying epithets to the horned owl, and we read of voraciousness, bloodthirstiness, blazing eyes, untamable savagery, and other attributes that are considered unattractive in wild animals. These words may be applied to man, who coins such terms, but not to wild animals, acting under the compulsions of their natural way of life.

My suggestion to people who can enjoy outdoor values is that they consider the horned owl as neither a feathered friend nor as a feathered fiend, but simply as a very distinctive and very interesting part of our outdoor heritage. As a wild species, it gives no allegiance to man nor owes him any, which is true of all wild species so long as they are wild—and which is as it should be. So far as I am concerned, the horned owl, by living its own life in its own way, has repaid me for any competition it has given me for "my" rabbits and other game (as a veteran hunter, I could claim losses as logically as anyone), for its depredations upon my poultry (our lakeside "old home farm" in South Dakota had perhaps "average" losses when I lived there), and for a fairly impressive collection of talon scars that I carry on my person. I would say that, even from a man-centered point of view, the horned owl belongs in our natural out-of-doors wherever its activities are not too much in conflict with human interests, and that persecuting it at random merely because killing it may be legal or customary to do so, is a mistake.

Leaving out the witchcraft and man's favorite label of "destructiveness," we have in the horned owl a superb predatory type, one of glorious wildness in a time when wildness becomes more and more priceless with each new encroachment of human populations and technology on what wildness we have left.

The hooting of the horned owl in a winter evening is reassurance to me that real wildness still exits, and I am thankful to live where I can hear it. Far from being a dismal or menacing sound, it has for me a freedom and beauty to make the air sing.

Our Little Wild Dogs: The Foxes

URING THE THIRTY-FIVE YEARS OR SO THAT foxes regularly have been part of my life, I have seen enough to make me careful about discounting the stories of red fox exploits. After allowing for exaggerations, faulty or questionable interpretations, and the role of chance in the events described, a substantial residuum could still be truth, or close to it. The red fox is a species that can show unusual intelligence. As concerns the behavior of an individual fox, I am not ready to say that anything can happen, but some remarkable things are possible.

I can claim personal familiarity only with the foxes of Minnesota, Wisconsin, Iowa, and South Dakota, which means certain subspecies of red and gray foxes. Red and gray foxes are animals of somewhat different habitats. In my region, rocky hills comprise typical strongholds for the grays, but grays are occasionally found far out on the prairies. Conversely, the red foxes prefer open land but may also be found in the forest. Indeed, we may see at times evidence of what could be severe competition between the two, with one species or the other increasing as the other species declines.

Gray foxes are not among our really "foxy" foxes. They do not look like what many of us think of as foxes. Even their tracks in the snow may seem more catlike than foxlike. They spend much time in holes—under ledges and bluffs—whereas the reds hardly enter holes at all except when they have young in the dens. The grays also have tree-climbing abilities, tendencies toward gregariousness in winter, and other attributes that we do not usually associate with our northern states red foxes.

I do not contend that differences in appearance and behavior between red and gray foxes make the gray foxes any less genuine as wild animals. The grays are adapted for a way of life

Audubon Magazine 57(1):14, 15, 16, 17, 27 (1955).

and are interesting, in themselves, as part of the out-of-doors. It is simply that a fox is a *red fox* to those people to whom the word "fox" arouses a special mental image in red and yellow, an image of a brushy tail almost as big as the fox body, of a certain creature bounding across a field or lying asleep on a sunny hillside or bedded down in a smartweed patch or on a snowdrift, or of the maker of straight-line tracks about a marsh or along a cattle trail. It is of red fox that one thinks in connection with fox hounds, sour grapes, and shenanigans in chicken yards.

It surely can be said that the red fox, with man's help, has made a name for itself.

In popular thought, the red fox has become the embodiment of cunning and mischief. It does have its playfulness—as do many other dogs, wild or tame, and many other animals that do not belong to the dog family. One need not be surprised because fox puppies romp, toss objects in the air, engage in mock fights, or do something else that they obviously want to do.

We must not, in any realistic appraisal of fox behavior, ignore individual differences. Ordinary red foxes may not show a great deal of originality, either in taking care of themselves or in their hunting. To plenty of the problems of living, they do not have particularly effective answers. Although they may easily avoid the traps spread over the countryside by unguided amateur trappers, professionals may trap dozens of them in a single winter by means of a limited number of effective trap "sets." Field researches have repeatedly demonstrated how well-situated populations of bobwhite quail and muskrats, two prey species toward which the foxes may show favoritism when they can catch them, may get along for months at a time without losses to foxes, the presence and efforts of high fox populations in their vicinity, notwithstanding. Most of the hunting by red foxes seems to be about as unimaginative and routine as hunting by the general run of hawks, owls, weasels, and other predators which may have decidedly lower learning capacities than the foxes. To all of these predators, *availability* of their prey is the main factor governing what they prey upon and how much. But once in a while an observer may witness the sort of headwork or "specialization" that gives foxes their reputation for foxiness.

My feeling that there are pronounced differences between the performances of ordinary and "outstanding" red foxes does

not imply that I know much about how versatile the "outstanding" foxes may be. I do not know whether they have their leg-
endary "full bag of tricks," or whether they have merely picked
up a few neat ones that they overwork. From analogies in the
behavior of "outstanding" coyotes and domestic dogs, I would
expect to find foxes having a limited though effective repertoire
and others that could be classed as all-round smart foxes.

It is often possible to learn much about an individual red
fox on the basis of sign (trails, uneaten food remains, feces, and
so on). Resident adult foxes confine most of their activities to an
area having a radius of about a mile. Their activities within this
area vary with the time of year, social relations with other foxes,
the presence or absence of formidable enemies, and their food
supply. Home ranges of fox families may overlap, but the centers of activity are usually well separated. Strange foxes may be
tolerated by the resident foxes or they may be driven off, and we
have here again the essentially doglike behavior of foxes.

In Iowa young red foxes are born in March or early April.
The mother may select as prospective denning sites old woodchuck or badger holes or parts of some complicated sets of holes
in a rocky hilltop used by generations of burrowing animals of
small to medium sizes. These she may rehabilitate many weeks
before the birth of the young, which first emerge from the den
holes when three or four weeks of age.

As the young grow, the ground about the den openings becomes packed, and trails radiate away into surrounding vegetation. Prey remains may or may not be strewn in the vicinity—
depending upon the nature of the terrain, the length of time a
den may have been occupied, the demands of the young foxes,
how good or poor the hunting may be, the types of prey brought
in by the adult foxes, the weather, and how much the den sites
may be worked over by scavengers. Feathers—easily detached
from the bodies of birds that foxes have eaten—tend to be conspicuous out of proportion to the birds actually occurring in fox
diets. The delectable meadow mice are usually so well cleaned
up that about the only evidence of them at a den may be in the
fox droppings. Sometimes, considerable numbers of the whole
bodies of the less-preferred white-footed mice and harvest mice
may be found, sometimes in heaps. Foxes may kill weasels,
moles, and shrews as they meet them, and they often leave
them uneaten at the dens or along their trails. Young foxes may
play with the mummified carcasses of these victims, but it

22

seems to take a very hungry fox to eat anything so patently ill-flavored.

If the foxes have access to much farm carrion of transportable sizes—dead poultry or small pigs spread over fields with manure, or even a stillborn calf or the leg bone of a horse or cow—this carrion may show up at fox dens. Miscellaneous den debris may include sticks, dry livestock dung, and old bones used for playthings.

Early in the rearing season, den sites are commonly changed after a few weeks, then changed more frequently as the pups grow larger and more active. A new den may be within a hundred yards of the one being vacated or up to a half-mile or more away. Of course, what the foxes do both reflects the alternatives open to them and the necessity of moving. Moves that are not forced outright by emergencies or the threat of danger appear to be due principally to the foxes wanting to get away from a befouled den or away from one that is proving to be too wet or otherwise uncomfortable.

In midsummer old den sites may be among the rallying (meeting) stations for a family of foxes, hunting as a family group. These associations, which may continue into late summer, doubtless have much value for the young foxes while they are learning to find their own food and picking up the elementary fox traditions concerning man and his dogs.

Late summer is a time when foxes may eat roasting ears (ears of sweet corn) in the fields, or fill up on fallen plums, or gorge on grasshoppers and crickets. The staple or much-eaten prey of foxes—the young of all mammals and birds taken regularly—reaches its annual peak of abundance, and hungry young foxes can bungle their hunting repeatedly and still have more opportunities coming up.

By early fall, the young red foxes are on their own and *family* sign, as such, may no longer be identified. The information we have from marked (ear-tagged) foxes suggests that the independent young move well out of the home ranges of their parents. The parent foxes maintain their "old homesteads" and comprise the most nearly permanent fox population of an area; they are, in particular, the individuals that make it their business to know what is what and where is where. The social intolerances of the red fox seldom permit these "vested interest" populations to exceed a pair per square mile in the wild. Transients drifting through or "small-time operators" discreetly hanging about the outskirts of defended territories (or trespassing when they can get away with it) may temporarily raise local fox concentrations in habitats attractive to them because of abundant food and cover.

As in mammals and birds rather generally, the less attached foxes, or "drifters," are the ones that have the least chance of reproducing successfully and the biggest chance of having tragedies befall them. They are typically the overproduced young of the past breeding season and, in naturally self-limiting population systems, the ones that are fundamentally expendable. Naturally, too, they do their best to stay alive, to do something with themselves, even in places where there is neither food enough nor room enough for them and where they know that they are unwanted. In time, however, a member of an established pair may become very old or ailing or be killed, and an upstart youngster may replace it, thereby advancing itself in red fox society.

In the matter of daily eating, the foxes, along with other opportunistic predators, may be expected to catch vulnerable prey animals as they meet them. These victims—rabbits, quail, pheasants, and other small animals—may be handicapped because of immaturity, illness, or injuries—notably, those crippled by gunshot during hunting seasons. A large proportion of victims fall in the category of parts of populations that exceed the capacity of the environment to accommodate them—the individuals that are too preoccupied with fighting or bickering among themselves to attend to the business of staying alive or those circulating restlessly in strange places or in the poorer grades of living quarters. Or the victims may be vulnerable to predation because an ice storm or a heavy snowfall has starved out a quail population, or the refuge cover of a marsh or weed patch or woodlot has been destroyed by fire, or something else has gone overwhelmingly wrong for the species preyed upon.

At times of exceptional availability of prey, the foxes make caches of uneaten material, which is sometimes buried under dirt, snow, or vegetation, sometimes left lying about. One may come on winter caches of foxes containing mice or rabbits which they may visit from time to time, whether they eat of them or not. The caches are fox "property"—as may also be miscellaneous prospective food items claimed by them, including carcasses of animals that the foxes had no part in killing. We have kept track of the ways that foxes have treated certain familiar carcasses during the winter—for example, the carcasses of ducks that died on late fall ice from lead poisoning or wounds. A given carcass may be mouthed by a fox or carried a short distance to a new site for caching; it may be dug out of a deep snowdrift and left on top, without any of it being eaten; or the fox may be hungry enough to eat half of a carcass; then it may continue to replant and dig out the remainder of the carcass for weeks. Our Midwest red foxes have a propensity for biting off and swallowing the frozen feet of carcasses of chickens, pheasants, coots, ducks, muskrats (also the frozen tails of muskrats), and so on, that they find, even if they do not eat more of them. They may vary this habit by biting off the easily detachable heads, as well.

The caching unquestionably has advantages as a racial trait for foxes. During periods of easy hunting, the foxes may seldom need to resort to "stored" food, but, when the hunting is difficult, the cache may still have something that is edible—unless it has spoiled beyond use of foxes or has been already cleaned up by crows, minks, skunks, mice, shrews, opossums, raccoons, dogs, or foxes other than the "owners." Foxes *can* starve to death, not only in northern wildernesses at times of food shortages but even, though rarely, in the more food-rich parts of fox range, such as in agricultural Iowa. When hunting is poor, there may be something dead lying next to a highway or out in a farmer's stubble field. A genuinely hungry fox is neither proud nor overly fussy about what it eats.

Now we come to the big question that over and over again confronts almost everyone having anything to do with wild foxes living in a modern human community: what *should* be an enlightened policy toward animals about which there is so much back-and-forth, around-and-around controversy, and about which there are such extravagant or emotional statements. I do not have any easy slogan to propose, nor any one simple answer, nor do I pretend to be able to express in words exactly what may be the public view, the public interest, or the views or interests of any group of citizens. The best that I can do is to try to summarize my own thoughts.

In the first place, whether we as individuals like foxes or not, we may well encourage more realistic ways of thinking about foxes. Human attempts to judge foxes or any other wild animals by human moral standards, as "good" or "bad," as willing helpers or as wilful saboteurs, do not bespeak realism.

25

Because foxes are predatory should not make them baneful, especially to people who are familiar with life processes. Predation is one of the main forms of natural exploitation, and it is by exploitation of something or other that all animals live. Foxes live as they can with what they have, according to their opportunities. If anything is wrong with that in principle, then life itself is wrong.

However, the fact that foxes capture and eat what man wishes to protect may, at times, justify human intervention— not because the foxes are morally bad for preying upon what man regards as his own but merely because it may be to man's advantage to prevent the foxes from doing certain things that would be perfectly natural for them to do. Defining exactly what is to man's advantage may, on the other hand, be quite a job.

The fox predation that man becomes aroused about is chiefly upon poultry or game. Depredations upon poultry *can* be expensive for the poultryman, but approved practices in poultry husbandry—such as keeping the flocks in enclosures— are automatic safeguards against most losses from foxes. The old farm standby, a good dog, can also be excellent insurance against foxes taking liberties about a farmyard. As concerns foxes and game, their relation may be complex and easily misunderstood, differing with the locality and the situation.

In Iowa, foxes are particularly blamed by sportsmen for shortages of ring-necked pheasants, bobwhite quail, and cottontail rabbits. That foxes may eat pheasants, quail, or cottontails should soon become apparent to anyone who pays attention to the food habits of foxes living in areas in which pheasants, quail, or cottontails are available as fox food. At least the cottontails may be staple prey of foxes in "cottontail counties." In no place where I have studied foxes, pheasants, and quail in Iowa and Wisconsin, have pheasants and quail been important items in the fox diet.

From the evidence boiled down, we may see that abundant populations of foxes are by no means incompatible with abundant populations of all three of these favorite Iowa game species. Some of the most thriving populations of pheasants, quail, and cottontails that I have ever seen were maintained *despite large numbers of foxes and other wild predators and despite human hunting pressure.* But these thriving game populations all had in common the tremendous advantage of suitable en-

26

vironment in which to live and to reproduce their kinds. In environment that is deficient in its necessities for pheasants, quail, and cottontails, these species do not thrive; furthermore, they stand by far the least chance of coping with predators and with inanimate dangers, alike.

The decade of the forties on my central Iowa study areas has been one of rather consistently high red fox populations. During the early years of the decade, we had excellent cottontail hunting. Since then, cottontail hunting has been poor. We have foxes but we also have cottontail habitats so deteriorated from intensified farming practices that scarcely a decent place remains for cottontails over whole townships of land. Central Iowa in the midfifties does have many jackrabbits, and jackrabbits rather than cottontails are what we may expect to have there as long as it continues to be more suited to jackrabbits than to cottontails—foxes or no foxes.

The usual reasoning of the outdoor public is that if the foxes are going to eat so many pheasants, quail, or cottontails, then, if we got rid of the foxes before they killed those pheasants, quail, or cottontails, we should have that much more game—or, at any rate, decidedly more game—awaiting us for the hunting season. As reasoning, it provides us with comfortable and satisfying panaceas, but it has an often overlooked factual disadvantage in that this is not the way things are apt to work out. The truth is that a great deal of predation suffered by wild mammals and birds in Iowa and neighboring states has little effect on the populations maintained by them even when the predation is heavy. The reason for this paradox is this: the young that are annually overproduced in relation to the available habitat are candidates for elimination either through predation or something else. Nature's resiliences and nature's shaking down of wild populations to fit their habitats make ineffectual much human effort intended in behalf of favorite species *unless that effort results in bona fide improvements of the habitat for game.* (And, even then, we have the weather and other factors to consider.)

Very possibly there might be, as a result of a substantial reduction of a heavy fox population, somewhat more cottontails maintaining themselves in the poorer of Iowa's "cottontail counties." Perhaps, there might be enough more cottontails under special conditions to make a substantial difference in the hunting. But on the basis of wildlife investigations carried on over the continent during the past three decades, I am certainly doubtful that persecution of foxes or of any native predators could substitute for livable habitat in the management of cottontails as game.

I recognize perfectly well that foxes can be overabundant from a number of viewpoints. For one thing, a serious outbreak of rabies in a community is no joke and may call for drastic measures when aggravated by high populations of the very susceptible foxes. For another, the mere presence of foxes in sufficient numbers to keep the public constantly aware of them has its undesirable by-products in endless complaints (justified or not) of fox damage, "viewings of alarm," and the emergence of "get-rid-of-them-once-and-for-all" philosophies.

As one who has had years of hunting and trapping in his past life, I suppose it is rather to be expected that I would not object to the more reasonable and humane types of exploitation of foxes by shooting them as game or trapping them as fur animals. What causes me pain is mass persecution of foxes as "vermin." It is not that the killing of foxes that may be too abundant for their own good is wrong; it is the hatred so often displayed by the public engaged in the killing.

As a naturalist, I like to think of foxes as creatures of beauty and grace and intelligence. Therein, I feel, lies their unique value to man. Years ago I would occasionally discover a farmer or hunter who felt the way I did about this and who would not be ashamed to say so. In our current era of fox abundance and jealous or frustrated hunters and farmers, one way of keeping out of arguments is not to say anything about the esthetics of fox trails.

Years ago I knew expert "still hunters" of red foxes, lean men who could walk all day, following tracks across blowing snow and guessing what they could not see. They sold the pelts of their foxes and were glad to have the money, but they did that sort of thing because they liked to do it. If they took bounty money, it was because they could use it, not because they wanted to live in a foxless country. Still hunting was a wholesome sport at which a farmer or a man from town could spend a day or two a week during the winter months, a sport requiring shrewd "know-how" as well as physical skills and stamina.

There are easier ways than still hunting to take red foxes,

and in view of the low market prices brought by the pelts in late years, many former still hunters no longer bother about going out for it.

I am sorry to see what looks like the passing of still hunting, along with some other old-fashioned things. Somehow, I feel that a renaissance of still hunting might go a considerable way toward solving our fox problems in the northern states, both for the foxes and for the people the foxes have to live with. At least, it might help more than bounty laws do to bring about a better public attitude.

II

OF MARSHES AND ISLANDS

WHEN PAUL WROTE IN HIS PREFACE TO Of Men and Marshes, *"for me, as an individual, no other natural feature has ever had the enduring attraction of an undespoiled chain of marshes in an undespoiled setting of glacial hills,"* he was remembering a certain South Dakota farm bordering the Oakwood-Tetonkaha chain of lakes and marshes which had been homesteaded by his Swedish immigrant grandparents. Although he referred to this farm as the "family farm," he grew up in Brookings and did not live on the farm until as a young man he tried for a few years to make a living there. Nevertheless, it was always for him the home place. It was where as a child he was taken by his parents on weekends and where later, as a teenager old enough to drive the family's Model-T, he went by himself to hunt and trap.

Responding as he did to marshes, it is not remarkable that he chose a marsh creature—the muskrat—as his principal long-term research animal when as a new Ph.D. he joined the staff of the Zoology Department at Iowa

ONE OF THE FEW UNDRAINED GLACIAL
MARSHES IN CENTRAL IOWA.

State College in 1932. His research on the muskrat during the following years resulted in a body of scientific writing familiar to any serious student of vertebrate ecology. But there was more. Essays of the sort represented in Part II of this collection were another fortunate outcome from the thousands of hours he spent working on marshes in all seasons.

An Iowa Marsh

OOSE LAKE IS A GLACIAL MARSH INTO WHICH runoff waters carry silt; it is a marsh where wind-blown dust settles and peat materials accumulate along with mollusk shells and other humble animal debris according to patterns set long before modern birdlife belonged to the ecology of any wetlands. Compared to the time required for the advances and withdrawals of glacial ice that fashioned the basin for this lake in central Iowa, the period of my familiarity with Goose Lake does not seem long.

Even so, since I first parked a Model-A Ford beside this marsh in 1932, it has gone through several radically different stages. Twice, during my observations, it has had lakelike open water and a maximum surface area of about 140 acres. Several times it has been dry or nearly dry with tracts of cracked bottom or puddles or frost-buckled mud and ice remaining in the low spots. At least once its dead stalks of cattail, bulrush, reed, smartweed, cut grass, and sedge have been swept by fire. Essentially the entire bottom has been overgrown with cattails and bulrushes. Or the emergent vegetation has been restricted to the shallows or to the deeper parts where the bottoms were exposed in late summer at exactly the right times for the germination of seeds.

I shall not say that I have always thought primarily of birds during the thousands of hours I have spent at Goose Lake. My memories may be of old things—a presettlement beaver jaw picked out of the side of a muskrat lodge or a bison skull cradled in the mud of the bottom. The memories may be of rotting bullheads that drifted to shore in windrows one spring following a winterkill; of snapping turtles crawling by the hundreds over muddy bottoms as they tried to adjust to a drought; of woodchuck dens and fox dens and mink dens and weasel tracks and

Chapter in *The Bird Watcher's America*, ed. Olin Sewall Pettingill, Jr. (New York: McGraw-Hill, 1965), 222–31.

a stream of ten deer mice leaving a muskrat lodge to bound away on the ice into the shore-zone vegetation. I may remember wooded islands that man had never tampered with enough to spoil their naturalness; or volunteer cottonwood seedlings that grew into a grove near the marsh during the years I was present. I may remember the nest of a red-tailed hawk in the cottonwood grove, and the great horned owls that frequented the nesting site of that red-tail the next winter and spring but did not breed; or the common crows that pestered the horned owls, circling and diving and sitting around cawing; and a Virginia rail that some students and I discovered on the ground in the middle of the cottonwood grove—a perfectly normal rail but one that didn't seem to know what it was doing there.

Birds are, in fact, represented in almost any scene on or about the marsh. In a sense, birds—that is, ducks—may be considered one of the principal reasons why this privately owned marsh has continued to exist as a marsh at all, why it was not drained long ago to make another Iowa cornfield. All of the years I have known Goose Lake, it has been leased to a club for hunting rights; and outside of the usually short, late-fall hunting season, when its ecology is right it can have a superlative abundance and variety of birdlife.

At Goose Lake the binocular season begins in March before the ice is out. The first mallards and pintails and blue, snow, and Canada geese rest in patches of water in the rotten ice or in water-filled depressions on top of the ice, and they feed in the nearby cornfields. These birds are high flyers and are inclined to settle down on the far side of the islands out of sight from the nearest roads. As the softening and opening up of the ice progresses, American coots and more ducks come, more mallards and pintails, together with the gadwalls, American widgeons, and green-winged teal, among the dabblers; and the ring-necked ducks, lesser scaup ducks, some common goldeneyes, maybe some redheads, and possibly some canvasbacks, among the divers. In my opinion the canvasbacks are the most elegant ducks of all.

The first mallards, pintails, and geese may largely push on, but more and more of the other early species of migrating waterfowl may come in. The newcomers are dominated by blue-winged teal, shovelers with bold markings on the drakes, more widgeons, and depending on the year, possibly by wood ducks as well. There may be some of the dainty, perky, dark and white buffleheads, ruddy ducks with their preposterously painted males, whistling swans lifting their heads and tootling, common or red-breasted mergansers and, if the water has food for them, a common loon or two or a flock of white pelicans. The pelicans may hang around for weeks if there are populations of stunted panfishes for them to feed on. The mergansers, which are popularly regarded as fish eaters, do not necessarily avoid a marsh if fish are not present but may feed upon water insects and other invertebrates.

When spring really comes, the red-winged and yellow-headed blackbirds stake out their territorial claims. The red-wings are more of the shores and fringing growths of vegetation—the weeds and brush and even trees of the adjacent land; the yellowheads like the deeper parts of the marsh where there is some water under their nests; but both species may fill up and quarrel over that which is not first-class habitat for either, with the yellowheads, by reason of their greater size and strength, generally able to take what they really want. Dry stands of cattails and bulrushes and sedges have their marsh wrens. Soras skulk and run over floating vegetation and fly weakly if alarmed. American bitterns poke through or stand in the wet meadow and the sedge and bulrush shallows to strike at frogs or whatever prey may come by, including meadow mice. The meadow mice, although hardly to be classed as water animals, often behave as such, whether moving down to marsh edge from higher land or actually living out in the marsh in the muskrat lodges.

Great blue herons may be seen standing or flying or alighting—giving the impression of being all wings and legs and necks. The fringing willows and box elders have their green herons, which seem to have even more neck than the other herons. The small but very-much-their-own-birds-living-their-own-lives least bitterns frequent both the shore zones and the deeper stands of cattails and bulrushes. Belted kingfishers rattle and fly along the edge from perch tree to perch tree. Black terns and the graceful white Forster's terns hover or swoop. There may be herring or Franklin's or Bonaparte's or ring-billed gulls.

Shorebirds on the mudflats or on the sand include the "peeps" (least and semipalmated sandpipers), killdeers, and lesser yellowlegs. "Jacksnipes" (common snipes) are scattered along the marsh edge or on the shallow flats that may barely protrude above the water out in the marsh. There are the dowitchers and pectoral sandpipers, and the phalaropes whirling in the water with their peculiarly webbed feet. And now and then, but not every year, ruddy turnstones, willets, avocets, godwits, black-bellied or golden plovers. If an observer is lucky, he may glimpse a big king rail before it slips out of sight or a common gallinule flying up ahead of a canoe cruising through the heavy bulrushes near shore.

A peregrine falcon or a pigeon hawk may fly over, pointed wings outlined against the sky. Occasionally, yet rarely, an osprey may hover and plunge or perhaps fly like a big gull with talons clamped on a fish. Rarer still is the sight of a bald eagle, almost always a juvenile, sitting on a dead stub.

Breeding-season birds are not always breeding birds. Some just loaf. I recall three snow geese that stayed on Goose Lake all summer, together with a white-fronted goose and one of the smaller *Branta canadensis* (probably *hutchinsii*). In addition to the loafers there are ducks stricken with lead poisoning, which leaves its victims at Goose Lake as on other Iowa waters. The ducks are unlikely to find much shot to swallow in the deep mud or peat of this lake's bottom. However, birds already carrying the potentially deadly shot in their gizzards are among those responding to the attractions of the marsh. The lead-poisoned ducks may comprise any of the gizzard-grinding species that come to Iowa, but the poisoned birds at Goose Lake run largely to divers—the ring-necked ducks, lesser scaups, redheads, and canvasbacks. They sit on the bases of muskrat lodges, flap along the surface of the water or dive if disturbed, and die when their turn comes. The feeding habits of the redheads especially predispose them to lead poisoning; the gizzard of a redhead may contain as much as a teaspoonful of shot, polished and partly ground away in digestive processes.

By midsummer the medley of bird sounds is basically one of redwing and yellowhead calls cut through by the melodious whinnying of the soras. Superimposed are the calls of the coots, the harsh cries of the black and Forster's terns, the squawks of black-crowned night herons, the pumping sounds of American bitterns and pied-billed grebes, and a miscellany of whistles and chirps that I admit I have never been able to identify. And often there may be the quacks of a mallard hen telling her ducklings what to do.

Fuzzy young yellowheads make short flights or climb

among the stems of emergent vegetation by means of their as-
tonishingly strong feet; least bitterns may flush out of the
bulrushes wherever a person wades or pushes a canoe, flapping
off to alight another fifty to one-hundred yards away; the mad-
dened terns, watching over floating or swimming downy young,
dive at the intruder's head; pied-billed grebes sneak off their wet
nest mounds, tossing coontail or bladderwort streamers over
the eggs as they leave; and the sound of coots skittering over
water comes from interspersed bulrushes and water up ahead.

Mallards nest on the muskrat lodges, as may ring-necked
ducks—though Goose Lake is close to the edge-of-range for
nesting ringnecks. There may be a ruddy nest built over the
water with the tops of bulrushes woven into a canopy, or, also
over water, a redhead nest of rush stems. Both of these species
are great parasitizers, laying their eggs in the nests of other
birds, and the clutches in their own nests may be laid too late in
the season for a successful rearing of the young. Very excep-
tionally, a pintail hen may be seen with a brood of flightless
young she hatched nobody knows how far away, possibly out in
a pasture or hayfield. Brilliant wood ducks may either nest in
the vicinity or just come to pass the time. Broods of blue-winged
teal are not at all uncommon. Young pied-billed grebes ride on
the backs of parents or trail behind. Coot chicks stay near one
or both parents or venture out by themselves, swimming and
feeding in their jerky way, very independent enterprisers even
when quite young.

Endless relations chain the eaters and the eaten. Maturing
damselfly larvae crawl up on the rush stems, break out, dry
their wings, and fly away, leaving the stems gray with the
empty larval cases. The terns, among others, hunt the dam-
selflies. Blackbirds, swallows, yellow warblers, yellowthroats,
and Baltimore orioles all search the marsh for insect food.
Young blackbirds, particularly during periods of abundance, often become the summer diet of minks and marsh hawks. Young
coots and soras and Virginia rails, the young least bitterns, and
the young of the common land birds of the marsh edge may also
be staple prey while their vulnerability lasts. The larger herons
and the bitterns too take what they can of vulnerable young
birds. As the young marsh birds grow, they may help to feed
the great horned owls frequenting the cottonwood grove or the
ancient trees of the island.

Fall brings a quickening of life processes and leisurely, lush times. Before any real southward movement begins, there may be a local massing of ducks on Goose Lake with birds coming in from all directions. They gather and loaf and pass on, the migration consisting of a dribbling through that continues for weeks before cold weather forces the spectacular flights. The blue-winged teal, particularly, may congregate by hundreds or thousands on parts of the marsh having a rich food supply of duckweeds and seeds of pondweeds, bulrushes, sedges, and smartweeds.

Shorebirds come, parades of them, the big and the little, standing, running, flying, alighting, calling, and feeding on the flats. The peeps run ahead as one walks the shore or come tamely up to feed within a few yards of a standing person. Jacksnipes may remain practically invisible on the mud and vegetable debris until an observer is almost up to them; then they are swiftly away with their scraping cry and erratic flight.

Blackbird flocks reach incredible sizes. I once calculated that a great roosting aggregate contained three-quarters of a million birds. A marsh hawk—usually in buffy juvenile plumage and acting hungry—sails low over the edge zone of the marsh or openings in the cattail stands, wheeling and dipping suddenly, and rather consistently not catching anything. Sometimes it succeeds, however, and redwing feathers, mouse stomach, or a rush stem with dried blood on it may lie on top of a muskrat lodge where the hawk stopped to feast.

By the opening of the hunting season in October the herons and rails are almost all gone. So are a lot of the ducks and blackbirds. Even so, Goose Lake might still have ten thousand ducks and hundreds of coots resting and feeding. With the approach of the shooting hour as the duck boats are being rowed or poled in their midst, the nearest ducks lift their heads uneasily. In the confusion of the first few minutes after the shooting starts ducks crumple in flight; then the birds gain altitude and learn where the hunting blinds are. For awhile perhaps five thousand mallards (plus pintails and other wary ducks) mill around at a height of a quarter of a mile. Finally they head for the Mississippi River on the eastern border of the state. By the next morning, the thousands of blue-winged teal are gone too and the coots represent the principal waterfowl remaining, feeding and swimming placidly as long as they themselves are not the target of gunfire.

The shooting does not terminate all opportunities to see

ducks during the hunting season. Flocks of widgeons or ring-necked ducks or lesser scaups may keep coming in from time to time, especially on a weekend when it may be assumed they have experienced hunting pressure farther north. They may come in high, glide or sideslip downward to alight in the open water, sit there ready to get up again if anything looks suspicious. Or the newcomers may be mallards that work around and around, almost alighting on the water, rising up to circle some more, veering this way and that, over and over, and then, despite all the preliminaries, arising to fly on out of sight. Or, if they have a storm behind them, the mallards may go through in string after string of immense flocks very high up.

After the close of the hunting season there may still be some open water, the larger patches of which may attract hundreds of mallards. They sit around the edges or swim in the center, rising to visit the cornfields to feed or alighting on their return with bulging crops. The raised rim of mud around the lake becomes slick and discolored from splashed water and droppings, strewn with feathers and parts of corpses—an occasional head or a leg or a breastbone with wings attached. Out on the ice sit the always opportunistic crows and maybe a visiting snowy owl.

As the oncoming winter shrinks the open water, the functional mallards leave, but there may still be some cold-tolerant mergansers—usually the red breasted but sometimes the hooded—and a few goldeneyes and other birds that stay late because they want to. There may be whistling swans to leave white feathers and big droppings on the ice. In addition there will be the birds that cannot fly—any of the ducks and the coots that have been gathering since fall.

After the last of the open water seals over, these luckless ones walk over the surface for a time; snow collects in tiny drifts from blowing past their bodies; crows peck, foxes sniff and eat heads and feet, and minks wrench and drag away. The bodies of blackbirds that did not leave in time to escape the first blizzards may lie in the reeds and cattails. At any open tile flow, the last jacksnipe sits or probes hopelessly. Minks lay down their tracks in formations of twos, threes, or fours and drag dead ducks and coots into holes. Smoky snow blows, and the sun forms new crusts, and in the intervals between cold snaps sometimes meltwaters swirl downward over enlarging ice cracks. Ice ridges buckle and minks drag feathery objects into the recesses and into the openings in muskrat lodges. Winter is harsh in Iowa.

In recent years the ecological pendulum at Goose Lake has swung all the way from a birdlife that thrived in a setting of cattails and bulrushes and muskrat lodges to a birdlife that existed in an open slough which had little to offer except a place on which to sit while feeding on the scant produce of the submerged or floating life. In lean years Goose Lake still had pondweeds, duckweeds, larvae of water insects, water fleas, crayfishes, frogs and garter snakes, some family groups of muskrats living in bank burrows, ducklings and grebe chicks on the water, hovering, swooping terns and swallows above the water, green herons and kingfishers in the trees, night herons and great blues wading in the shallows. Although it was by no means birdless, the multitudes of birds dependent upon cattails and bulrushes were simply not there any more, and no one should have expected them to be.

The collapse of the emergent vegetation was all according to the rules of order governing marshes and life of marshes. Everything happened naturally; the marsh went through its natural stages and so did the marsh life with it; and, as long as man does not interfere overmuch, the story may be expected eventually to repeat itself—a lush period again following the not so lush. Goose Lake may still be an undrained marsh rather than just one more Iowa cornfield.

Of Marshes and Islands

ARSH ISLANDS OF THE NORTHERN STATES AND northward are often distinctive land areas, as wild as the marsh itself. If sufficiently inaccessible, they are as nearly unvisited by man and by man's domestic stock as any of the higher ground about a marsh or lake that we may expect to find in long-settled human communities.

Heavy growths of certain weeds of cultivation may at times take over parts of these island areas having soil that is frequently disturbed, as by ice, wave action, or rodents. Marsh islands may have their timber cut and be more or less littered with trash and may have shacks or cottages built on them. Still, they are not apt to be put under cultivation, and many of them are man-free for months or even years at a time, except perhaps during the hunting and trapping seasons.

In spring and summer marsh islands are often the retreats where concentrations of wildlife find undisturbed breeding conditions when they need them most. This is not to say the crowded occupants of island breeding grounds live with idyllic security just because they are relieved from human intrusions—though relief from the latter *can* be among the greater blessings that wild things enjoy.

The laws of life may apply to the island dwellers even more conspicuously than to the dwellers of the real marsh, because of the even greater crowding that may take place on the islands. There is friction between crowded individuals, there is exploitation of the exploitable, and there is death on the islands; but with man largely out of the scene, the processes of living and dying have the sanction of timeless order. Of course, modern man is of Life, also, yet his dominance and his faculties for upsetting so much of the rest of life serve to rule him out of what we think of as "natural" relationships of living things.

There could hardly be, it is true, human dominance more complete in its way than the dominance of some islands by fish-eating birds. A small island may have almost nothing alive on it except cormorants and the scavengers, predators, and parasites associated with cormorants and their foods. The cormorant islands reek of dead fish, of excrement, and of combinations of odors unpleasant to the human nose. The ground has its dead birds in all stages of decay and dismemberment, together with the fish bones and the whitewash over all. Similar domination by one or a few species is to be found on island rookeries of pelicans, gulls, and other kinds of colony nesters.

I am not saying that one must be able to enjoy close contacts with some of these rookeries to appreciate their meaning as natural phenomena, to appreciate their manifestations of life in, yes, its beauteous aspects. For the foulness by human standards of the rookeries need not detract from the grace of gulls in flight nor of cormorants in the water, nor from the spectacle—at a distance, if one prefers—of living creatures living as their kinds lived on islands in the ancient seas, lakes, and marshes. We need not impute conscious dignity to wild animals because they look dignified (when they are not squabbling or trying to choke down something too big to swallow), but theirs is still the dignity of the millions of years that they and their behavior patterns have persisted.

Island rookeries are not always dominated by single species to the exclusion of a varied fauna. I have seen many heron rookeries having hundreds of nests concentrated on island areas of a few acres. While it was plain that the herons were there, at least some of these islands were rich in other life. Away from the groups of trees that were loaded with heron nests there lived many of the usual animals of islands. Beneath the heron nests would be hunting grounds for predators and scavengers, and a windstorm violent enough to blow nests out of trees might really bring down some exploitable food resources.

One central Iowa island of not much more than an acre had during a single breeding season a rookery of black-crowned night herons, a pair of great horned owls, a mother mink and her family of young, one or two raccoons, a lone fox squirrel, a considerable number of woodchucks, a population of wood mice and cottontails, and in the bank burrows of the island and of a smaller island adjacent to it, nineteen family groups of muskrats. The plant eaters found what they needed in the island growths, the herons ate fish, frogs, and invertebrates, the horned owls raided the heron rookery but subsisted chiefly upon prey from the mainland, the raccoons and minks lived upon crayfishes of the shallows. The minks also exploited the young muskrats forced ashore by the population tensions of overproduction. In addition, the island was a favorite loafing ground for pheasants and had attractions for crows and wood ducks. The burrow systems of the dense population of muskrats thoroughly undermined the banks in places, and the upper parts of the muskrat burrows were used by minks, raccoons, woodchucks, and cottontails. The woodchucks dug right into the chambers of some of the muskrat burrows.

The time came when the herons no longer returned to the island to nest, but that apparently made little difference to the other vertebrates of the island. The island continued to have its pair of horned owls, though these always seemed to be unsuccessful in their breeding. The pheasants always showed partiality for it and so did the minks, and it might have a covey of quail or a visiting deer or a red fox from shore some hundred and fifty yards away. It had the downy woodpeckers and nuthatches and chickadees and brown creepers of woodlands. Its horned owls and minks fed upon the water birds of spring and fall flights. Its dead stubs afforded perches for the rare peregrine falcon or osprey.

I camped on the island the afternoon and night before the duck hunting season opened that year when there was such a concentration of muskrats in the island burrows. High water had killed the cattails, and the stubble of last year's growths stretched out across the open water in almost all directions from the island. In late afternoon ducks were everywhere on the duckweed-covered water: the not-too-trusting mallards and pintails and the thousands of blue-winged teal, feeding, tipping in the shallows, sitting in bunches, exercising their wings, and losing themselves to sight in shadows and hummocks and dead vegetation. Muskrat wakes broke quiet surfaces, some close by, some so far away that they resembled but moving lines. As light smoke from the supper fire spread out over the water from one side of the island and as the haze of evening came on, more muskrat wakes appeared, and the animals lay and sat amid the duckweeds and pondweeds. They ate on the few remaining live cattails and bulrushes and foraged in the shore zones. I counted between forty-five and fifty simultaneously using a hundred yards of shore, while more walked or ran with hunched bodies in the background of sloping shores and abrupt banks. Somewhere would be one bounding along a trail toward the water, vegetation protruding from its mouth and dragging on the ground.

When the night grew chilly, I pulled another thickness of heavy blanket around me. I could not see much over the water, but hoots of horned owls and the clear quacking of mallards carried through the general anonymity of night sounds.

For two or three winters I jumped a red fox with some regularity during my visits to this island. From the fidelity that it showed toward the same escape routes—the routes used depending upon the direction of my approach over the ice—I suspected that I was observing the behavior of an individual fox. Then, on a fall day before freeze-up, I prowled the edge of the island hunting ducks, and there a fox similar in appearance to the one I had been jumping stood looking at me from a chokecherry thicket about fifteen yards away. It disappeared in the thicket, but when I got around to the opposite side of the island, it ran out of a gully, stopped on the bank, and turned to watch me, though nearer than before and standing wholly in the open. We looked at each other for about a minute, until the fox slipped along the ridge of the bank into the brush again. I wondered if that island fox might not have come, in the course of my repeated visits without overt acts, to recognize my scent as that of a harmless animal, the shotgun in my hand notwithstanding.

In the following spring a litter of fox pups was born in a rehabilitated woodchuck hole about in the center of the favorite winter fox retreat. The teething pups came out and chewed on the chokecherry stems around the den entrances and cleaned up the prey remnants to the extent that scarcely anything was left in sight but coot and blackbird wing feathers and a cottontail foot. The island itself offered limited feeding opportunities for a hungry fox family that spring, and for some weeks I could not see where the food was coming from, even in the minimal quantities that the pups apparently were getting. The sign that gradually took form with the progress of summer was of a fox-scented trail leading from the island's brush down through the fringe of cattails and bulrushes, a watery trail straight across a hundred yards of duckweed-covered bay, to another trail through cattails and bulrushes leading up to the mainland. Any foxes crossing from mainland to island had to swim part of the distance, carrying prey or not, and I am sure that foxes have had easier ways of life. Still, the mainland dogs did not get out to the island dens, the little foxes grew to be big foxes, and my snooping about holes and trails seemed to occasion no worry.

I remember once when my presence on the island was taken more seriously. The surrounding shallows were drought-exposed, and I saw a big old raccoon digging crayfishes out of the mud of an open space. I was about eighty yards from the raccoon on a windy day and intentionally moved to an upwind position to see if the raccoon would catch my scent at that distance. It reared up in my direction, wheeled, and bounded off toward the mainland as fast as if I had shot at it.

So far as a dominant form of life on this island is concerned, neither the herons of years ago nor the enterprising flesh eaters that lived with and followed them quite seem to fit the role. The herons did not make out as permanent residents, though I do not know why not. The horned owls were permanent residents but their reproductive failures illustrate the marginal quality of this island environment for them as a species; as adult birds they thrive there, and I can visualize the place as always having its horned owls, as being the sort of place to attract new owls each year if something tragic befalls the old residents. Yet it lacks the nesting facilities to perpetuate its own horned owl population—it has no hollow trees large enough for horned owl nests. Lacking hollow trees, the owls need nests of red-tailed hawks or crows for their own nesting, and the redtails and crows of the neighborhood will not nest on such a small island as long as the owls are so much on the scene, and the owls are always somewhere around.

The raccoons and foxes can be prominent parts of the island's life, and so can a white-tailed deer when it tramples snow and browses in a sheltered corner. So can the minks when they take over muskrat burrows and leave muddy tracks about holes in snow and ice, crisscross new and old snow with trails, and drag over to the island the bodies of waterfowl and muskrats from anywhere on the marsh. So can the muskrats when the periphery of the island becomes almost a continuous set of burrows. Despite everything predatory, any winter snow that has lain on the island overnight in condition to take and keep tracks may be expected to have cottontail tracks. But no one of these species so much characterizes the life of this particular island in my mind as do the woodchucks.

45

Woodchuck holes occur both on top of and along the sides of the island, from the highest points down to the water's edge, under root tangles of trees, in thickets, in nettle patches, under glacial rocks, and on open ground. The burrows are newly dug, they are weathered, they are rehabilitated old burrows, they have brittle woodchuck bones in the earth heaps—and muskrat and rabbit bones, or maybe raccoon or skunk bones. I never could make satisfactory estimates of the island's woodchuck population at any one time, nor even judge whether the diggings and trails were of one or more family groups—there are often heavily used, interconnecting overland trails between main burrow systems. I do know that young chucks are raised there, and probably some surplus young go to the mainland. Passage of woodchucks to and from the mainland occurs, during both drought exposures of the shallows and periods of high water.

A little island on the home farm in South Dakota had its numerous muskrat burrows, its minks, and, whenever it had land connections, its visiting skunks. Its trees had the small tree birds of lakeshores and the herons and the kingfishers. Instead of a population of woodchucks to burrow the higher ground, it had a population of Franklin's ground squirrels ("gray gophers"). Its ground squirrels, like the woodchucks of the central Iowa island, were not marooned from the adjacent mainland any more than they wanted to be, either at times of high water or low. They left tracks on the sand or drying mud of exposed land connections, along with the skunk tracks and mink tracks and heron tracks and shore bird tracks; and I did not consider it an astounding sight to see ground squirrels swimming.

The home-farm island has many memories for me as a campsite, and I do not forget, either, how often I would go out of my way just to visit it, to see what was new and interesting, if not profitable from a predatory standpoint. The memories of herons squawking overhead in the night and ground squirrels whistling during the day while I fished for bullheads from the bank are all in the picture, and so is a memory of a weekend planned for duck hunting but spent instead in the dripping gloom of a tent during an almost constant downpour. What I remember still more, when I really think of the island, are the little scenes from brief visits: the tracks of crows, muskrats,

46

mallards, and minks in wet slush; the mink tracks in snow almost everywhere, leading to old ground-squirrel holes, into snowdrifts, under gooseberry bushes, across open spaces; the bloody holes in the ice and the clam shells over muskrat channels; the fresh bubbles and food remains floating under new ice. A freeze-up caught our flock of about a dozen Pekin ducks across the lake from the farmyard, and while the ducks were waddling on the ice, the minks killed every one of them and dragged the bodies into holes, mostly into holes on the island. That gave the island a special attractiveness for minks for some weeks thereafter.

The droughts of the midthirties killed the island's trees and transformed it into a mainland hill, whereupon it became covered with buckbrush, and the mallards took it over for nesting. After the water came back, muskrats again lived in bank burrows, and minks again worked the edges. The island again had integrity as a wild island, but some of the terms of its biotic equation had changed. Two decades after the great droughts a few small hardwood trees were rising above the buckbrush.

I know several islands in northern Iowa marshes offering a wide variety of ecological conditions. These have their higher ground partly covered with big trees and their lower ground with a brushy, grassy fringe grading off into wet meadow. The more extensive or interconnected island groups have essentially their own animal life. Fox squirrels, horned and screech owls, woodpeckers, and the common woodland songbirds nest in the trees, shrikes and brown thrashers nest in the plum thickets, and tree swallows nest in the dead willow fringes. Raccoons, red foxes, skunks, minks, weasels, ground squirrels, meadow mice, deer mice, shrews, woodchucks, meadowlarks, ducks, and garter snakes occur on either the higher ground or the low ground. Near the meadow's edge live the rails, blackbirds, muskrats, and crayfishes. The trails of eaters and eaten lead in and out of the water and everywhere in between. The low grassy or brushy islands can be among the most life-rich of the northern prairies and on which duck nests may be concentrated by the dozens or even by the hundreds. About these islands one may hear the whinnying of sora rails and the calling of frogs and toads.

Low-lying peninsulas may also have wildlife populations

similar to those of the islands. The area having the most consistently high populations of breeding waterfowl, minks, and
island-type life of which I know in northern Iowa is a sprawling,
irregular series of peninsular meadows indented by shallow
bays. It is so inconveniently accessible to motorized man as to
have—with respect to human disturbance—many of the advantages of the less accessible of marsh islands. It is in the middle
of a four-section tract of land where geese loiter during migration and where willets and other big or rare shore birds are apt
to appear if they appear at all in that part of the state.

Separate mink families may live on almost every peninsula.
Raccoons, skunks, foxes, opossums, crows, gulls, terns,
kingfishers, marsh hawks, and herons work the meadows and
uplands that they find profitable working; and the local crayfishes are staple diet for all of these except when something else
happens to be more available.

It is rather plain that the advantages isolation offers to
island-dwelling forms are advantages only of degree. Seldom
does the isolation of an island give anywhere nearly complete
protection to anything. The minks having their young on
islands stand a better chance of rearing them without molesta-
tion by dogs, foxes, or coyotes, but both wild and tame dogs
may reach the marsh islands. Even if they do not, there can be
killing of minks by minks as crowding becomes pronounced.
The island-nesting birds suffer a certain amount of loss from
the minks and other mammalian predators that are already
there, and it takes real isolation to be valid against the predators
that fly. Even the great rookeries of island-nesting birds may be
vulnerable to raiding by crows, ravens, and gulls in the absence
of predatory mammals. However, absence of members of the
weasel and dog families on islands may encourage some of the
greater concentrations of the ground-nesting birds. But then, if
a mink or a fox or a coyote ever does get over, the status of the
concentrated island-nesters may be worse than on the
mainland.

We need not assume that the island dwellers are uniformly
helpless against those racial enemies by which they are frequently visited. Some—such as the larger herons and geese—
can be dangerous for ordinary predators of mink or fox or raccoon sizes to molest. Less formidable defenders may still be
capable of more mobbing power than predators care to invite.
Moreover, the individual birds or groups of birds among the

48

colony nesters show much variation in their own security or breeding success. One trend of the evidence coming out of wildlife investigations is that predation is largely centered on the parts of populations having the poorer places in which to live or on the parts of populations having trouble with their own kind. What goes on in natural relationships on marsh islands is much in keeping with the evolution of the participants, of the eaters or the eaten.

We come back to the idea of islands being among the better places for wildlife if only to the extent that they may keep man away during some of the critical months of each year. I have known marsh islands in Iowa and South Dakota that were covered by growths of poison ivy entirely sufficient to discourage people from wading or rowing out to them, to mess around irresponsibly among the duck nests. In the Precambrian Shield, many islands are bounded by such sheer rock faces that only people having mountaineering ability ever climb up on them. These are retreats of species that particularly do want to be left alone, such as peregrines or eagles nesting far above the water. The rough country north of Lake Superior has islands so high and so precipitous that they resemble great pillars.

Some areas in the Precambrian Shield have islands nearly everywhere in wilderness lake chains, well away from places where people go, away from the can-littered canoe routes. They may be barren islands or partly wooded or heavily wooded, left to the mergansers and goldeneyes and whatever else there is to fly, swim, or wade out to them. Islands may lie near the mainland or be connected with it by rocky or sandy shallows or by a continuation of marshy fringes or by bogs or willow swamps. Islands may grade into peninsulas. There may be a moose in the lily pads, a bear in the blueberries, red squirrels in the pines, a beaver lodge on one side and deep water on another. On islands or on peninsulas, the minor distinctions between them are ignored by the creatures finding them accessible and livable.

Although the rock islands of the Precambrian Shield may be thought of as being almost as permanent as the Earth—composed as they are of some of Earth's oldest rocks—the islands of glacial debris are likely to persist only until the next glaciation. Many of the latter have had time to realize most of their possibilities as living places for island species of plants and animals.

The islands of modern deltas and stream channels, in contrast, sometimes do not last long.

On the windswept and stream-flooded Netley marshes south of Lake Winnipeg, the higher and more permanent of the islands offer refuge to marooned mammals during high water. They have their deer and coyotes, their mice and minks; and prey and predators live close together when the waters force withdrawals from the surrounding lowlands. Life may then become a matter of finding the safest hummock or tree crotch or unsubmerged hole and waiting out the flood.

Along the lower bank islands bordering the central channels, the muskrats stay as long as they can as the water rises in their burrows, and they open up the tops and enlarge the chambers just below the surface of the ground. As the water nears the top or covers the ground, they must come out to build nests anchored in whatever vegetation there is along the banks, or out in the marsh, or to sit in the scrub willows, or to lie quietly, trying to remain in the neighborhood, somehow. If there are helpless young in the banks, the mother may deposit them, one by one, all or only part of the litter, in a drier place outside. Young of swimming sizes may lie in a pile in the water, in a hole or in a nest, the lower ones withdrawing to climb on the others, until some become too weak to withdraw any more, and their bodies lie, a platform of dead young flesh supporting the still-living young flesh. At high flood, all the muskrats of the low bank islands may be gone, the old and the young and their nests and sitting places. Dead and living bodies may float away, toward the lake along the flowing channels or off somewhere across the marsh, over the channels and banks and washed down vegetation.

The channel islands themselves come and go in consequence of wave washings, the action of ice, or changes in flow of streams. Mud bars or sandbars remaining until annual plants have a chance to colonize them are used by wildlife and may often show areas of new plant growths fed upon by muskrats, beavers, and waterfowl. If they last a few years longer as islands, they may be covered by grasses and sedges, by saplings of ash, willow, cottonwood, and similar stream-edge hardwoods. Old channel islands have old forest on them but their relative impermanence is still betrayed by the undercutting of the big trees by the current in one place, together with the building of new bars in another.

Dense stands of aquatic plants separate from the bottom muck and rise up to form another type of island. Floating cattail islands support in their dry and tangled upper parts not only the muskrat lodges and nests that one expects to find in cattails but also populations of garter snakes, mice, and nesting birds, and sometimes even such dryland animals as striped ground squirrels. These islands are most conspicuous on some marshes that are about to become open water lakes and may represent virtually all of the broad-leaved cattails able to stay alive after the dying of the stands remaining rooted to the bottom.

The muskrat lodges may themselves be islands, having their own insects, spiders, snakes, turtles, bird nests, toads, mice. Meadow mice live in and about some of these lodges much as the muskrats do, swimming, climbing, and, if pursued, diving. Such mouse populations are truly of the marsh, the year around, reproducing their kind over the water, feeding on exposed rootstocks of bulrushes or on the summer greenery. It is tempting to conjecture how muskrats came to be muskrats in the course of geologic time, insofar as they are in skeletal structure but overgrown meadow mice. The meadow mice have a good start on the adaptations of muskrats.

When I lived on the old home farm amid the lakes and marshes of east-central South Dakota, a place known as the "Goodfellow island" was a peninsula rather than an island. It was a tract of a hundred acres of pasture, with little marshes between hills and a big marsh bounding one of its four sides. Open-water lakes having reedy or rushy coves bounded the other three sides. (When the water first came back after the droughts of the midthirties, this "island" was almost surrounded by marshy waters, but that does not represent its usual state.) The neck of land that made it a peninsula lay at one corner of our farm, and as the pasture was owned and used by a jovial neighbor, it was always within my regular home range for prowling, hunting, and trapping.

The Goodfellow island, not being at all conveniently near the owner's buildings on the far side of one of the lakes, usually had on it only livestock requiring a minimum of care. Often, I must have been the only person to be on it for weeks at a time. It was one of the places where coyotes could still live in some safety during years when they were all but hunted out over the

51

whole county. Except at the boundary of an alfalfa field on our land, most wildlife there had little more access to the products of human agriculture than they must have had during the days of the Indians and the bison. The bark-fed cottontails sat in primeval innocence in the lakeshore thickets and let me pick them off one by one with any firearm that I might have along. Not so independent of man were the prairie chickens that boomed on the hills in the spring and roosted in the slough grass in winter. They required a proper ecological balance of undisturbed wildness and such blessings of cultivation as the corn and small grains that a farm could provide.

Muskrats usually thrived in the deeper bulrush and cattail marshes of the hills during the breeding season, along with the minks and ducks and blackbirds. The shallower of the marshes tended to go dry in late summer, which was all right for the minks, ducks, and blackbirds but not so advantageous or even endurable for the muskrats. The latter could find themselves in trouble before midwinter. They gnawed holes out through frozen bank burrows or the sides of lodges, fed upon debris of dry plant stems or upon the few rootstocks or tubers of marsh plants that they could reach from above. I dug out nests in snowdrifts and followed trails in snow, trails along the lakeshore from one ice heave to another. Victims finally died of fight wounds, hunger, and cold, were eaten by other desperate muskrats or by minks or mice or crows, or lay sodden and exposed to view by the spring thaws.

Besides the minks, the place had a regular predatory fauna of weasels and badgers and many striped skunks. The staple foods of these were characteristic of both uplands and lowlands of east-central South Dakota: the rabbits, mice, and ground squirrels, the beetles and grasshoppers and water insects of grasslands and marshes, the crayfishes and frogs and snakes, and the fishes of the surrounding lakes.

With or without man, Goodfellow island was a natural sanctuary for native wildlife. Everything seemed fitting for a naturally self-sustaining combination of animal communities and everything seemed to fit. The colonies of nesting red-winged blackbirds, each with its own territorial subdivisions, the meadowlarks nesting on the hills, the screech owls and the flickers in the lakeshore cottonwoods, the pair of marsh hawks, the few pairs of crows, the garter snakes and bull snakes and snapping turtles, all represented animals adjusted to what they had. At times of natural crises, the aquatic life furnished tremendous quantities of food for the creatures able to exploit it, and then many opportunistic hunting and scavenging forms came from the surrounding areas. The drying of the big marsh usually bounding one side meant concentrations of herons—not only of night herons from a rookery across the lake but also great blues that seemed to be drawn in from the entire lake chain. The semiannual bird migrations always meant new food for flesh eaters, especially in the form of the ailing ducks sitting around at the last of the spring migration and fall migrants that could not leave at freeze-up.

Storms put much edible matter on the beaches. I often saw in the broken plant debris of beach drift choice fishes that were so clean and fresh that I was tempted to take them home to eat but never quite dared to: walleyes, ten-pound northerns, and big sunfishes. Just before one freeze-up, a windstorm washed up hundreds of snapping turtles. An old note describes snappers being tossed in the drift at intervals of every five to twenty feet along a six-hundred-yard stretch of rocky shore. The stranded snappers would try to get back into the lake, always, so far as I could see, unsuccessfully. On their sides and backs and in normal positions, those snappers were still there at dusk, when the spray was beginning to freeze, still numbly moving their feet. And there the freeze-up caught them, and their bodies were iced over, gathered snow, and the snow blew around them as they lay like so many lakeside rocks. Then, with thawing of their ice and snow covering, they were turtles again, and not rocks, and the winter's hungry flesh eaters pecked and gnawed and wrenched.

My memories of Goodfellow island are linked with memories of my personal depredations upon its wildlife because that was the way in which I lived. I remember one quiet June afternoon and evening for the thousands of lake buffalo spawning in the shallows—and for the killing, cleaning, and salting of a barrel of fish—enough to last us well into the summer. Yet, if anything, my memories of some things that did not profit me directly are even stronger, as of spring holes in the ice near shore packed with minnows, perch, and bullheads too small to eat.

I was on Goodfellow island a great deal at night during my trapping years. It was not only on one of the most direct routes home at the end of some of my traplines and offering passably easy walking, but it also held the allure of the not-quite-to-be-expected. My hopes were always to be able to sneak up on a coyote howling from a hilltop, but nothing like that ever worked out for me. Nevertheless, I would stand a better chance of seeing a weasel or a mink abroad in the night or at least some of the more commonplace of night creatures—if nothing more than jackrabbits—disporting themselves a little more openly than during the day. There might be night sounds hinting more of mystery than the daytime sounds. There might be some kind of adventure.

One mild and brightly moonlit night in early December, I was cutting off toward home and saw a huge skunk ambling between the hills—a five-dollar piece of fur in those days. The only firearm I had with me was a heavy revolver loaded with two cartridges, so I ran after the skunk, trying to get in a position for a certain shot. The skunk speeded up and so did I, the back pocket of my hunting coat half full of wet muskrat skins slapping as I ran. As I caught up, the skunk would dodge or threaten to throw scent, then run off again, to dodge some more, never holding still long enough to give me good aim. So in the December moonlight we played the old game of predator and prey up and down the hills, until the skunk ran straight ahead and I ran beside it, hip boots pounding the frosty ground. As we ran together about five feet apart and about as fast as we both could go with what we had left, I got off a shot, and the skunk went into a roll of waving tail and feet and black and white limpness. I gave my prey time to die, returned the revolver with its remaining cartridge to the holster, shucked off hunting coat, rolled up shirt sleeves, and got out the skinning knife for one more job under the midnight moon.

I have not been on Goodfellow island for many years. In the midfifties I saw from a distance that as in other parts of my old farm neighborhood its hills were plowed and planted to corn. Perhaps, some of its long-undrained marshes have been drained. It still had no buildings, however, and I think that man is unlikely to change it to the extent that it will no longer offer comparatively good environment for native wildlife. Its strategic location and the rough land of its edges assure it of some permanence in that respect. Whether I ever go on it again or not, I am glad that it exists.

I know that some people whom I respect maintain that natural beauties are valueless unless human eyes may be present to appreciate them, and to such opinions my only reply is that not all of us feel that way. To me, the fact of being is justification for natural beauties. One who loves the out-of-doors should not necessarily have to visit islands or peninsulas in person to enjoy the thought of their existence. These islands and peninsulas are a delight to me in that they may maintain so much of their wilderness integrity, in that they may be so much a part of naturalness where naturalness belongs.

Wilderness Islands of the North

ORRTÄLJE SKÄRGÅRDEN IS AN ARCHIPELAGO that extends eastward into the Baltic Sea from the vicinity of the small Swedish industrial city of Norrtälje. Norrtälje itself lies about fifty miles northeast of Stockholm. For something like one hundred thousand years much of Scandinavia— including this area—lay crushed under the weight of the last glacial ice sheet. Today, some four thousand years after the melting of this colossal overburden, the land is still springing up at the rate of about a foot and a half each century. It is literally rising out of the sea.

As a visiting biologist, I became acquainted with the Norrtälje area during two spring months spent at Uppsala University's nearby field station on Lake Erken. I was particularly eager to see as much as possible of what remained of the wild in this part of Sweden. Away from the farmlands and villages extend natural woods, rocky hills, bogs, swamps, and lakes—a great deal of only partly tamed wilderness. It is true that the original population of wolves and bears are gone, that many other wilderness life forms are depleted in numbers, and that lumbermen's cuttings and roads invade some of the wildest tracts. Still, the land and water in secluded places continue to represent some aspects of the former wilderness.

Here and there, from deep woods to the Baltic shore, can be seen badger sign—the long-used dens in rocky crevices, the superficial diggings, the tracks, and the droppings. The large proportion of plant food eaten by these badgers offers a remarkable contrast to the carnivorous and insectivorous diet of the North American species.

Beneath the roost trees of the local tawny owl (a relative of our American barred owl) lie castings made up of remains of the same types of small vertebrate prey that a barred owl would be

Natural History 71(5):8–17 (1962).

likely to eat under similar conditions. Feeding perches of the tawny owl will also have under them feathers of a small bird, dropped fragments of a mouse or shrew, or egg masses of frogs—discarded in the same way that North American predators commonly discard unrelished items.

Red foxes range the meadows, cutover tracts, and shore zones, leaving their spoor along trails, and bounding away when surprised.

In the woods the hazel hens—the nearest European equivalent to our ruffed grouse—look and act like our own ruffed grouse. Also sheltered here are big forest grouse, the capercaillie, and droppings made up of pine needles attest to the marvelous digestive system of these birds. Overhead, familiar woodcock dash back and forth in their erratic, mating season flight.

The deeper woodlands, more nearly unbroken, contain forest in which a stranger might become thoroughly lost. Only game trails lead into these depths. Here are the cow-sized hoofprints of moose, and conifers and hardwoods with bitten-off twigs and stripped bark show where the moose had fed. A marten has worked on the forest floor, and in the wet spring snow are lynx tracks.

Many places may remind one of the prehistoric hunters who ranged over land then newly emerged from ice and sea. The Norrtälje area has dozens of Stone Age burial grounds, and the mounds and stone memorials are now high up on banks that must not have been much above the waters of the coastline at the time of the builders. Thoughts of wild human hunters and their prey come easily as one walks ridges and hilltops and peers down through forest growths toward the lakes and bays. It is easy to think of old ice and new land, the slow advances and withdrawals of ice sheets, freezings and meltings, the comings and goings of a subarctic sun over centuries and millenniums, life adjusting again and again, in its own ways, wherever it belonged. It is easy to think of glacial ice as being a part of the Scandinavian scene in its geological manifestations, if not in its immediate presence; it is easy to think of it not being so very far away at all.

Whenever I found myself in a position to look out upon the nearest islands of the Norrtälje Archipelago, I could see that the islands themselves showed evidences of being biotic continuations of the mainland's peninsulas. Both islands and peninsulas hold about the same kinds of living things, or sign of living things. Alike, their lower rock tops show the fish bones and scales of otter droppings, fresh and weathered. Buzzard hawks, crows, gulls, crested grebes, goosanders, tufted ducks, a few pochards and scaups, and scattered pairs of mallards are to be seen. There may be mute swans in the reef-fringed waters.

When the archipelago is viewed from the right places, it is seen stretching farther and farther out to sea; wooded islands at first, and then islands with little vegetation on them. In the distance they look like a broken line, and if one looks out far enough, it is hard to be absolutely sure what is land and what is water.

As guests of a party of ornithologists, my wife and I had our first opportunity to go out onto a Baltic archipelago one sunlit Sunday in the middle of May. In a chartered fishing boat, during one of the rare calm interludes in Norrtälje's spring, we spent nearly all of one day.

Our expert fisherman-pilot just kept to a marked navigation channel for an hour or two as we headed outward. The vegetation on the islands that we first passed was chiefly of coniferous or mixed forest. As we went even farther out, the coniferous forest tended to be replaced by hardwoods. Ultimately, not much remained that could be designated as forest at all. There were irregularly distributed hardwood trees of small size, thickets and mats of juniper and deciduous bushes, birch zones, heather patches, mossy growths, lichen-covered rocks. Where nothing could grow, the rocks and gravel lay exposed, but something adapted to the role usually grew wherever growth was possible—even in the most wave-beaten places.

In studying these islands I thought of the continuity of the pioneering thrusts and adjustments of all living things, of life insisting upon living as it could. The changes in vegetation, which became apparent as we moved deeper into this archipelago, were rather similar to those one could see while moving from low to high altitudes in mountainous regions. Close in along the coast (the equivalent in altitude to a region of lowlands or foothills), were all of the denser forest growths. Farther out (or up), came the birches and thickets and then the lesser tundra or alpine plants. Finally, far out (or far up), were nearly bare rocks.

Out in the archipelago the rocks showed beneath the surface of the water as grayish, yellowish, or greenish blotches, which faded into the most indefinite outlines or sometimes into no real outlines at all. Our boat passed so close to some of these blotchy formations that I nervously wondered if our fisherman-pilot had seen them as he steered along the outskirts of island clusters, islets, and huge protruding or partly hidden boulders in a section of Swedish coastline into which very few people ever ventured.

As we poked along carefully, searching for a place to anchor, we could look down through the water at blue mussels and slimy rocks and sodden pieces of wood. Ashore in this rocky region one might in some places walk with ease from islet to islet if careful not to step in water that would slosh over boot tops and not to slip or to lose one's balance.

The rockier islands of fair size—from one to several acres in area—were mostly occupied by nesting colonies of different gull species. The gulls sat on the island rocks unless we approached close enough to put them, protesting, into the air. Some of the islands had nests of eider duck as well as of gulls. Sometimes the eiders seemed satisfied with little more than token nesting cover. At least, there they were, in patches of low vegetation, tucked in angles made by rock edges, the nests hardly even partially concealed. Perhaps the eiders were running out of choices for nest sites or perhaps they chose to nest near gulls for the protection against raiders that the noisy gull colonies might afford. In either event, many eiders nested on gull islands.

The most popular islands for nesting eiders, however, were those having thickets of juniper, carpets of heather, and arctic-alpine types of small plants irregularly covering the rocks. In the shallows about these islands or on the wet rocks around the edges, we could see eider droppings consisting of crushed mussel shells.

Eiders would not be everywhere, even in the archipelago belt so obviously suited to them, but on one island we found so many eiders that we decided to walk along the shore to avoid disturbing them unnecessarily. Despite our care, incubating females kept flushing from their nests. Then we would cover the exposed eggs with a light layer of ground litter to make them less conspicuous to egg-eating birds. Four eider hens flushed from their nests in one patch of heather some ten feet in diameter as we cut across a point on the way to our boat. For variety, a shoveler hen, almost an exact counterpart of the shoveler hens that nest in the Dakotas, flushed from a nest among those of the eiders.

All the flushed eider hens alighted on the water a couple of hundred yards away, where they sat until we left. As the boat again headed deeper into the archipelago, we watched the eiders gradually return to the island; first a few, then they were all back.

A pair of sea eagles circled over the islands and the open sea. We saw three eagle nests in small trees; one was old and falling apart, with most of the nest on the ground. The islands in the vicinity of these eagle nests had no nesting colonies of gulls or eiders, but we did flush a black grouse from near the one recently maintained eagle nest that we visited. This was on an island on which were boggy spots, heather, and grassy growths—much the sort of terrain that a black grouse would be apt to choose on the mainland—and there the bird was, with miles of water between it and anything else resembling its habitat.

There were other mainland creatures in the archipelago, too, so far out that I wondered how they got there. Way out on the principal eider island on which our party landed, a viper was sunning itself on a flat rock. It tried to slip away as we approached. I wanted a picture and so headed it off, and the snake turned to strike at my boots as I blocked its movements in all directions and stood over it while taking the photograph. My last view in the ground glass was of two and a half feet of glistening black snake disappearing into the heather.

The question of what a viper might be eating on this island, so distant from the mainland, was soon answered. We saw vole sign—burrows, paths, cuttings, and droppings—throughout the grass, heather, and low growths. The interest of other predators in the vole populations of these islands was further demonstrated by vole bones and fur in faded, wintertime owl pellets that lay on some of the rock surfaces. The pellets looked like those of short-eared owls, but they could have been those of the tawny or Ural owl or perhaps even the hawk owl or the snowy owl. The owls in question necessarily had to be among those that hunt where the cold winds blow and where some ground drifts over with snow while other ground stays bare; where the nights are long and daylight is restricted to a few hours of sun and to long dawns and twilights.

We traveled far into what is known as the outer archipelago of Norrtälje Skärgården, but never so far that we could not see still more islands and islets—clumps and strings of them like distant reefs—lying still farther ahead. The quiet sea and its emerging land became part of a hazed-over, dreamlike horizon. Something very old and fundamental seemed to characterize the setting, something older than the Baltic Sea itself or any one glacial or interglacial stage.

I searched in my mind, as I have often done in other parts of the world, to identify some feature with what James Norman Hall had referred to as the "spirit of the place." Perhaps it could be identified with the winds or the waves, with their capabilities for dominating violence. Or it might be identified with the rocks coming out of the water or lying just beneath. Despite the calmness of the day and the visibility of the subsurface rocks, it was not hard to imagine being out on these waters when deadly turmoil might constitute the spirit.

Yet, more truly, some form of life should characterize this outer archipelago. Besides the eiders, gulls, and sea eagles, we saw velvet scoters, tufted ducks, mergansers, and black guillemots. We saw razorbill auks that our hosts likened to stubby, flying cigars as they arose in front of the boat and swept past us. Flocks of hundreds of long-tailed ducks sat on the water, and the males called. As I think now of our spring day's visit, I can make only one nomination for the spirit of the place—the calling of the long-tails, one of the most wildly beautiful sounds in nature.

At times, these calls would come as a distant chorus, rising and falling, building up and letting down. Or the chorus might come from a large flock nearby, to build up and come over in a wavelike "ah-ah-oo-lee, ah-ah-oo-lee." The Swedes refer to this call of the long-tails as a spring song, or a hymn of the islands and of the sea. Whether one thinks of it as that, or as a breeding season ritual, it is its own essence of the wild and free.

The flocking long-tailed ducks do not even stay to breed in Norrtälje Skärgåarden. When their spring migration is over, their calling will no longer be the spirit of the archipelago. But, in the memory I carry with me, this will always be the sound of the islands and islets, of the gentle sunshine and long reaches of quiet water and indistinct horizons reaching north and east.

Of Marshes and Peace of Mind

NE THINKS OF THE END OF A DAY AS BEING A time for peace of mind, and a sunset may have not only its own beauty but its symbolism of peace. My memories of sunsets are not confined to marshes, but it has been on marshes that I have been aware of some of the feelings coming nearest to complete peace of mind of which I seem capable. Others have had similar experiences. I think of an internationally known sportsman, an industrialist, who for years, planned vacations so that he could spend part of them on an Iowa marsh during the trapping season. When asked if he were not becoming too old for that sort of thing, if he might not die sometime out there on the marsh, he asked in his turn: "What better place is there to die?"

Air and water do not need to be quiet to induce peace of mind if one be receptive, but there is symbolism in Nature's quiet, too. The reference to still waters in the Twenty-third Psalm, the final paragraphs of Longfellow's *Hiawatha*, and countless other passages in our literature reveal fundamental longings of people everywhere.

My own memories of sunsets and peace of mind in wetland settings differ greatly in details. They include memories of hunters poling in to shore, of kidding and laughter; of trappers almost flying over the ice in boats on runners, coming in to rest, warm up, eat, and talk; of scenes with no other people or traces of other people in sight.

I think of one in which I was a predator. Late one afternoon by the most careful crawling through marshy cover and over wide, bare stretches of mud, I worked right into the midst of a small flock of feeding mallards. I had to walk around the marsh to reach the canoe and then return over the water to pick up the birds that the shooting gave me. Before undertaking the hour and a half stalk, I had thought that I probably could not get away with it, and then, in the mellowness of accomplishment, I shook the water off the mallards and laid them on their backs in the bottom of the canoe and looked upon them and across the marsh toward the sunset. A couple of small islands were reflected on the water, and the sunset colored the whole western view.

I was anything but a predator while watching another sunset, when ducks were alighting by the hundreds in one of the few marshes having water during a great drought. Those ducks were little more than population remnants, and at that time I was doing all I could to discourage anyone from duck hunting. I stayed at the marsh edge until I could no longer see anything of the ducks and could hear only their calls and the sound of wings in air and splashing in water.

I have memories of other sunsets at times when I was simply living my life, such as it then happened to be. I might be driving home the cattle along the lakeshore back on the South Dakota farm. Or, as a biologist, I might be making a marsh-edge camp before dark and trying also to keep track of the fighting and wandering of muskrats out on the ice at the time of a population crisis. I might be trying to catch fish for food and not doing well at it. I might be sitting in a car writing up field notes or just sitting and watching.

I often recall the coming of a night on Upper Red Lake in northern Minnesota, long ago when I was young. I was returning to my trapping headquarters on the Tamarack River after having gone to the largest town within reach by canoe to buy a half-case of shotgun shells and several crates of dried prunes.

By late afternoon, the water was becoming quiet and, toward sunset, it was smooth—mile after mile of it—with a slow and rhythmic undulation. I still had a couple of hours of paddling ahead of me to reach the cabin, and ice crystals were forming on the burnished water, tiny needles growing as the sun went down. I kept dipping the paddle as fast as I could and still get full power out of it. Dip, pull, scull, over and over, my knees spread and braced in the center of the canoe, the sound of my heart and breathing mingling with the sound of swirling water about the paddle.

As dusk came the ice needles tinkled with the rise and fall of water over the lodged driftwood out from the beach and hissed as the canoe rode through them. I was happy, though a little uncertain. I knew that the hissing would grow louder and that by the time I reached the Tamarack there might be thin ice to break—perhaps just a little ice, enough to outline the wake of the canoe and to wear away some paint without actually wearing through the canvas. Perhaps the ice would be cutting ice before I could find a place having a land trail to the cabin. When I reached a trail, I could leave the canoe and pack home in darkness the precious crates of prunes.

That memory is one of peace and of problems. The problems were not overwhelming, but there were the uncertainty and the awareness of things still to be done. So it seems to be with man almost always, almost anywhere. Peace of mind exists, or can exist, but I do not know how much any of us can attain any complete peace. It seems such a relative quality, whether that be due to me, to the nature of the human mind, or to the nature of peace itself. Anyway, I can find some peace in thoughts of water seeking its own levels, of buds unfolding, of fruits ripening, and of wild things staying wild; and I think that the outdoor values that have meant so much to my life are among those worth preserving in modern civilization and those that every well-intentioned person should have a right to share if he wishes.

III

OF WILDERNESS AND WOLVES

WHEN PAUL WAS FIFTEEN AND THREE years from finishing high school, he decided to go up into the Canadian North the following year and begin his life there as a hunter, trapper, and naturalist. Of his campaign to gain parental permission for this venture he later wrote:

> I . . . began a long and persistent campaign to obtain permission. I must have worked on this for months, whenever I was home, at mealtimes and in the evening.
>
> Why should I continue going to school when I knew what I wanted to do? All I would need up in the wilderness would be an axe, a rifle, traps, and the simplest equipment for cooking, sleeping, mending clothes, and so on—all to be taken in one canoe load. I would build a log cabin with a rock fireplace and skin windows. I would live on wild meat as the Indians and Eskimos did. During the long winter nights I would light the cabin by means of a wick in a dish of animal oil. It was all so logical—I pointed that out innumerable times—and why should I not know what I was doing?

Paul's mother did not give in to his arguments and ultimately it was agreed between them that he would finish high school before

A MAGNIFICENT PREDATOR LIVING IN
A NORTHERN WILDERNESS WHERE IT BELONGED.

going off into the North alone. At eighteen he did spend a winter alone in a northern wilderness but it was in the Big Bog country of northern Minnesota rather than in the Canadian North. (Many years later, as the parent of two teen-aged sons Paul expressed profound relief the neither son proposed going alone into the Canadian North.)

The first essay in Part III, "Fall and Winter in Northern Minnesota," is a narrative account of Paul's first wilderness experiences. This essay comprises portions of "Fall in the North Woods" and "Winter in the Big Bog," two chapters in The Red Gods Call.

Next is "Canadian North," published first in Discovery: Great Moments in the Lives of Outstanding Naturalists, *John K. Terres, editor, Lippincott Press, 1961, and later in* The Red Gods Call. *Paul never did spend a winter alone in the Canadian North for reasons stated in this narrative.*

The essays which follow "Canadian North" are of a different sort. They are chapters from a book entitled Of Wilderness and Wolves, *still in manuscript form at the time of his death in 1962. In his words, they are about "the hard-to-define and hard-to-maintain values that tend to be lost with increasing human domination of the earth."*

Paul chose to write about wilderness areas in the North because he knew these from personal experience; and he chose wolves as the central characters because he was intensely interested in wolves as wilderness creatures.

These essays about values, written toward the end of his life, are, of course, philosophical. Nevertheless, he drew, here too, on early memories as is suggested by one paragraph in his preface: "Extending back are my own memories of long winters, of northern lights and sinking frost lines, of drifting snow over plains and ice, of stillness of spruce and cedar swamps, of snare wire and Newhouse traps, of weariness, loneliness, and beauty. Much of my life up to graduate training was that of a professional hunter and trapper. I was a predator, myself, and lived close to the land."

The first essay, "Of Wilderness and Wolves," the one bearing the title of the book, was published in The Living Wilderness *in two parts, autumn 1969 and winter 1970–1971.*

The second, "Of Man and Maturity," was published in Atlantic Naturalist *in winter 1968.*

The third, "Of Algonquin Park and a Wolf Named Dagwood," has not been published elsewhere. Paul's experiences in Algonquin Park in 1960, narrated in this essay, were his last experiences in any wilderness area.

Fall and Winter in Northern Minnesota

I WAS EIGHTEEN AND IT WAS FALL 1920. THIS was for me a leisurely time as I paddled my canoe up Thief River and Thief River Falls in northwestern Minnesota. I had never been there before, but somewhere, in some suitable place, I was going to spend the coming winter fur trapping. A winter in the North Country. That was what I had been planning for since my early teens.

It was the mellowest of Indian Summers in late September. The leaves were turning color and the air was delicately fragrant with wood smoke. I knew freedom and peace, and I knew my body had toughened. I headed upstream toward the Red Lake Indian Reservation, enroute to whatever places were as far into the Big Bog as a canoe could take me.

After the last of the white settlers' buildings disappeared from sight, there were few signs of man from the river for mile after mile. Tops of dark conifers protruded more and more like great pinfeathers from the hardwood forest. Slowly the panorama changed. The stream borders became marshy. There were growths of wild rice; there were muskrats and ducks and muddy game trails between water and woods. The game trails showed small footprints and large ones, of rabbit and mink and skunk, of deer and doglike animals. The doglike tracks seemed narrower and less fleshy of foot than ordinary dog tracks. These were the wolf track characters I had learned to look for. I could not always be sure of them when I saw them.

I particularly remember Red Lake River and Lower Red Lake for their campsites during that Indian Summer, so benign and comfortable after the passing of the mosquitoes. At one place I heard a peculiar tinkle. It came from a pool so full of minnows that they looked almost solid in the rays of a flashlight. When pike drove through the massed minnows, the minnows popped into the air to fall back into the water with the

71

tinkling sound. I remember awakening one morning with a ruffed grouse looking at me through the opening of my little cruiser tent, about a yard from my face.

Another night I pulled up to a sand ridge at the marshy outlet of Lower Red Lake. I was tired and did not bother to put up the cruiser tent but just wrapped up in blankets under the canoe. A storm whipped sand into blankets, clothes, and hair— and into a kettle of boiled ducks. In the morning I rinsed out what sand I could from the ducks, but the duck grease still held enough so that my teeth gritted with every bite.

Here, along the sand ridge, the wooded lakeshores stretched away and disappeared into water and sky. As I cleaned up and shook out and repacked, the sun hazed over; the sky and quieting water became suffused with yellowish light. I had thoughts of being alone on a beach between a marsh and a sea in an otherwise manless world. Except for me and my outfit, the scene could have gone back a million years.

My next camp was on a hilltop on which tame ruffed grouse strutted or budded in the aspens. Other wild creatures also had the tameness of those that never had reason to fear man. Between my hilltop camp and the lake beach lay a narrow strip of white cedar swamp. The outermost cedars extended out on the sand ridge of the beach to within ten to fifteen feet of the water's edge. There were no cut stumps; no axe or saw marks; no cans, bottles, cigarette packages; no junk either along shore or in the strip of cedar swamp. Neither were there "deer lines" where deer had overbrowsed the lower cedar growths, though a lakeside trail had tracks of deer as well as of wolves.

The lakeside fringe of cedars was so solid that I had to push through it to enter. Inside, the sights and smells gave the impression of primeval life and a clean and wholesome and beautiful decay as a part of life. Trunks of the living cedars were two feet or more in thickness; seedlings and saplings grew where they could. Dead and living cedars and balsam fir stood or leaned partly uprooted or lay on each other. There were open spaces through which one could walk, and tangles of trunks and boughs and roots that one walked around or climbed through or over. Mosses and lichens covered everything—hanging, clustered, growing in mats. On the ground punky downlogs lay partly sunken into the swamp floor, partly settled into themselves, and partly overgrown with peat moss. Still older down-logs were only peaty ridges, going back into what they had come from centuries before.

The chipmunks gave this place active life in the daytime. They sat, they fed, they streaked over the down-logs and the sand ridge. But in my memory of the cedar swamp, nothing can compete with the lynx. As the local deity of an ageless sanctuary, the lynx did not quite lose its unreality by any full materialization.

I was standing at the edge of the lake scouring the supper grease from the frying pan with sand when I first heard the lynx squalling, perhaps a hundred yards away. More and more squalls, closer and closer, until they came from directly in front of me about ten feet away. The lynx was inside the wall of cedars, and it squalled and squalled so that I knew exactly where it was. I knew it was standing with its forefeet on the sand ridge, watching me through the hanging cedar boughs.

The dusk became dark as I waited—not knowing what I should do, feeling more than a little spooked, yet intensely wanting to make the most of the experience.

The lynx was still not quite distinguishable in the rays of my flashlight, though the squalls were coming almost from within reach. After ten minutes or so of this I began to worry about my flashlight batteries, afraid they might burn out before I reached my hilltop camp on the other side of the cedar swamp. In going through the cedar swamp earlier, in the shaded daylight of late afternoon, I had slipped off a log and had gone up to my hips in soft peat. In fact, I had had to grab a limb to keep from going deeper. That swamp was no place in which to be groping around without a light—lynx or no lynx.

After a few more minutes of indecision I walked straight for the wall of cedar with lighted flashlight. My approach made the lynx lose some of its brashness. It became silent, but I am sure that it stayed close for a time and kept me company partway across the swamp. There were shiftings of shadows that could have been due to no movements of mine. Twice I glimpsed what I thought was a square face with tufted ears among the shadowy tree trunks and the drapery of moss and hanging boughs.

Halfway across I was sure the lynx had left me. I worked carefully the rest of the way on fallen logs to the base of the hill; climbed the hill to the tent; spread out my bedding; and appraised the extent to which my wet socks, pants, and underwear had dried on me since the afternoon's slight mishap in the swamp. One last squall, quite faint, came from the lakeshore.

During the night something carried off a new slab of bacon left, forgotten, near my wet-down supper fire on the beach. The bacon was no sad loss, having been a poor buy—too wormy to be appetizing and too expensive to throw away outright. Its disappearance settled the question of what to do with it. It could have been taken by a wolf but it may have been taken by my lynx.

I like to think about my experience with that big curious squalling cat—that very special wilderness creature living where it belonged in its own proper wilderness.

As I settled down alone in my trapping headquarters on the Tamarack I felt a little scared. I did not know what to expect of cold as winter progressed. I worked rehabilitating an unoccupied cabin on the Tamarack River, chinking and nailing. I cut, carried, and piled firewood and put things where I could find them after the snows came.

The cabin needed a stove, so I made one out of an old oil barrel. The boiler door of a derelict small steamer on Upper Red Lake served for a stove door. I recall shooting the rivets out of the hinges with a deer rifle and having the problem of standing close enough to center the bullets on the rivets offhand but back far enough to be safe from flying metal. This oil barrel was set in a log-boxed foundation of sand on the floor.

For a bed I spread a small tent over a layer of wild hay on the floor and covered it with woolen blankets. I weighted down the blankets by piling logs along the bottom and one side and in that way had a makeshift sleeping bag—not as nice as an eiderdown, but I did not have and could not afford the eiderdown.

As fall turned into winter, I tried some psychological resistance to the North Woods cold. My reasoning was that if I postponed changing from cotton to woolen underwear as long as possible, I should be better acclimated to the cold when it really became severe. All that this idea did for me was to keep me shivering for about a week and to encourage thoughts that the northern cold must have a uniquely penetrating power even before it had brought much more than hard frosts at night. Finally I put on my woolens and the climate seemed to moderate.

I prowled in the woods and did some loafing while I had a

chance before the fur season began. Some unharvested onions remained in what had been a garden during the summer, and these I gathered one day as snowflakes came out of the sky.

I ate when hungry, as much as I wanted to, as my developing eighteen-year-old body needed food. My winter's supply of venison was packed in layers of ice in a barrel outside the cabin. This, together with flour, provided the energy-giving essentials for a trapper's diet.

The transition from fall to winter was very pleasant, very peaceful. Snow fell steadily, settling down through windless air. Ruffed grouse, almost as tame as the chickadees and Canada jays, walked into the cabin clearing. They sat in the aspens eating buds, in plain sight of the cabin. When alarmed, they flew off, dodging among the tree trunks.

Beavers and muskrats came out on the ice and tracked up the first snow. Trails of minks ran along the stream edge from one open patch of water to another. Bounding weasels marked up the snow almost everywhere. There were tracks of snowshoe hares and red squirrels and deer. There might be something else; a porcupine trail, the sign left by a horned owl killing a snowshoe hare, the tracery of mice and shrews and small birds. There were fox tracks in straight strings and crooked trails, going through or laid down as the foxes had hunted or investigated wherever they had wanted to.

One morning I saw, not fifty yards from the cabin door, the trails of three timber wolves on the river ice, each track the size of my closed hand imprinted in the few inches of snow.

The Tamarack River cabin itself was nothing to promote sentimental memories; it was only a place to stay, with comforts that were at times scarcely minimal for a trapper's needs. As winter temperatures went down, crystals would form on the water in a pail in the corner of the room despite the oil-barrel stove. The oil barrel and stovepipe would redden, and I would watch the hot places to judge when to shut the damper in the pipe and bank the stove door with sand. At bedtime I would fill the oil barrel with slow-burning green aspen logs and tightly bank the stove door. The greater outer cold would press in, and everything freezable would freeze.

I went to bed with a stocking cap and most of my clothes on except mackinaw and leather-topped rubbers; on the coldest nights I put on everything I wore outside. Over me would be the substantial weight of fourteen woolen blankets alternated with layers of newspapers. Whenever I shifted positions the mass crackled, but weighted down by logs as it was, it never slipped off to expose me to the subzero temperatures of the night. I would work into the pile of blankets and papers until my head was almost submerged, shiver for a while until body heat warmed the inside, and go to sleep easily and completely. In the morning my breathing aperture would be frosted, and perhaps my body would be outlined in frost on the topmost blanket. This may not sound like the comforts described in hotel advertisements, but I felt refreshed each morning and never had any illness all winter.

Early morning routine would be to push away the sand with which the door of the oil-barrel stove was banked and so let the draft in on the smoldering shells of aspen logs. As the blaze caught I would put in hot-burning dry tamarack or spruce or white cedar. By lantern light I would chop through the inches of ice on the water pail, whittle or hack off some frozen venison, and mix baking powder and flour for pancakes or biscuits. Sometimes I would warm up whatever was in the stew kettle and eat that for breakfast.

In the evenings while writing letters or reading or reinforcing the thinning places in socks, I sat beside a lantern some five to eight feet from the alternating glowing and cooling oil barrel. At that distance I could open up mackinaw or shirt collars and button them again in a practically automatic manner. If I had to, I could get up and move; usually I did not unless something on me was beginning to scorch or my hands were becoming too numb to write or sew.

About once a week I would have a bath and a clothes washing. The upper part of the cabin would be wet with steam, and the log surfaces nearest the stove would glisten; the inner cracks between the logs and the angles deep in corners stayed frosted and gathered more frost. Underwear, shirts, and socks hung as close to the stove as I dared put them; I would feel by hand the hotter parts of drying clothing to make sure that nothing became too hot.

At times I craved unobtainable sweets and luxuries. For five or six weeks I was without sugar or dried fruit and ate large quantities of pancakes—just as they came out of the pan—for what little sweetness I could imagine in them. When I next could buy sugar I cooked up a granular fudge that a schoolgirl would have thrown out, and this I ate not only in chunks but also as frosting on baking-powder bread and biscuits.

The baking-powder products were baked in an improvised oven consisting of a rusty frying pan kept for this one purpose, some nails in the frying pan, a greased pie tin on top of the nails, and an outer pan upside down over pie tin and frying pan. The nails in the frying pan elevated the pie tin so that hot air could circulate below. The dough was put in the pie tin to bake, and the bread or biscuits emerged with charred bottoms. After the charred bottoms were trimmed off, the rest was fairly good, especially with butter or syrup. If there was no butter or syrup, the bread or biscuits were still food for one hungry enough not to be finicky.

The piquant flavor of fried grouse, initially delightful, eventually began to make my jaws ache. About the only way I could still enjoy grouse meat was to use it, flavor diluted and modified, as a base for stew. Old but edible remnants of mustard and horseradish in the cabin helped me to eat grouse meat after I could hardly tolerate it but still needed it for food.

Snowshoe hares were always fat and delicious and a staple food of which I never tired, but I did not always have them and often had to depend on grouse or the venison laid up frozen from the fall hunting.

No venison I cooked was delectable with the single exception of a rib roast baked in the "oven." This was good, but it made such a sticky mess of the pie tin and old frying pan that I did not feel another roast justified the work of cleaning the utensils. Hence I continued to fry or boil the venison. The meat was very wholesome, very nourishing. It could be and was eaten strictly as food—for my body's sake and for the warmth and energy required by the cold, by the snowshoe trails, and by the axe work. I ate the venison with mustard and horseradish, thankful that it could be made to taste less like venison. Toward spring I thawed out and jerked (thereby salting and drying) the rest of the venison and ate it when I had to.

Although I had previously boiled a variety of meat in big kettles at earlier camps, the stew kettle truly became part of my life at the Tamarack River cabin. There, with months of cooking behind me, I experimented with stews when I had the ingredients for experiments. A luxury stew might contain a bacon square along with wild meat, canned milk, canned tomatoes, rice, onions, and canned corn. The tomatoes would curdle the milk, and the rice would stick to the bottom with continued cooking, but this stew could make me so pleasurably drowsy at the end of a day on snowshoes that I would lie on top of the bed and sleep until the cooling of the oil barrel awakened me. I might blow out the lantern and get under the covers, aware that unless I refilled and banked the stove I would have a fire to rebuild in a most frigid cabin in the morning, but I did not care.

For variety in meat I might have porcupine. I had read in an outdoor magazine that porcupine flesh should be fried in hot grease. Therefore I fried it in hot grease at arm's length and with mittens protecting my hands. The spattering grease burned off the stove.

The one expensive food item I had to buy was dried fruit. I would try to ration a newly opened box but never could make rationing work with anything so lusciously different from venison and my flour products. I had no trouble eating a pound or two of dried fruit a day—which, while good for me, sometimes could become financially burdensome. A pound of prunes or peaches at forty or fifty cents cost about one weasel pelt or—if I needed cash to the extent of taking a job cutting cordwood for the Chippewa Trading Post at Waskish—about three hours of axe work and lifting logs onto a bobsled. The more special dried apricots, pears, and figs cost still more at backwoods prices. Once after pondering the price mark on a can of blackberries, I invested sixty cents and carried the treasured article to camp. The canned blackberries proved to have such a suspicious appearance of spoilage that I was afraid to eat any. It hurt to dump into the snow that equivalent of a weasel and a half or of four hours of cordwood cutting. But I could always count on venison to fill me up if I ran out of fruit or sugar or butter, and a little jar of horseradish had power in it.

A tremendous amount of woodcutting had to be done to keep the oil-barrel stove putting forth heat while I was in camp. This cutting required every precaution to prevent the axe from glancing. If the axe glanced in very cold weather, a piece of frost-brittle steel might break from the blade. Once after chipping away a little half-moon, I had to work for hours to get the bit sharpened down so it would cut again. There was also danger of injury from glancing blows: when the axe did glance, I had to retain sufficient control to guide the blade so that it missed leg or foot. It could be tricky, especially when I was tired and each stroke took just a little more concentration.

Burning green aspen for night logs resulted in an accumulation of creosote in the stovepipe, and this drained through the joints to the outside of the stovepipe. The creosote would dry and sometimes smoke as the pipe heated, or glow as the pipe reddened on a cold night. One night the creosote accumulation blazed, filling the upper part of the room with smoke. I did not like this glowing residue or the smoking so tried to keep the excess creosote scraped off.

One midwinter afternoon I was across the river cutting wood and happened to look over at the cabin. The roof was on fire around the chimney. I went back as fast as I could run with snowshoes, ran into the cabin with snowshoes still on, grabbed a pail of water and heaved it up at the blazing roof. The water came down on me. I got the snowshoes off and ran outside. My wet clothes froze, but I could not be bothered by that. I climbed up on the roof and put out the rest of the fire with snow. The fire had burned a yard-wide hole in the roof.

I went back across the river and cut down an aspen that must have been a foot and a half in diameter at the level of the snow. Out of this I chopped two rough planks about four feet long and four inches thick, and with these I mended the roof.

As I looked at the mess inside and smelled the rich odor of smoke and wet charcoal, I started working out my compromise with physics and chemistry. After the fire burned low in the oil barrel and the stovepipe cooled, I took down the pipe and replaced it in an upside-down position so that the creosote would drain back into the stove rather than to the outside through the leaky joints. The pipe took a bit of forcing in places, but when the job was done I could rebuild the fire with more confidence than I had known for weeks.

The snow often fell heavily and continuously for hours at a time. In places out of the wind it remained undrifted and fluffy from the middle of November to early spring. It piled up in perpendicular walls on fallen tree trunks. It loaded the tops of spruce and cedar. By late winter the fluffy snow reached a depth of about five feet on the level and lay even deeper where gentle wind eddies piled it without packing.

Immense drifts combined with ice ridges lined the shore of Upper Red Lake, and the more or less bare lake ice reached a thickness of between four and five feet. At the river near the cabin, I had to cut through as much as four feet of snow and three feet of ice to reach a new source of camp water whenever an old water hole became unusable. It took temperatures of twenty to forty degrees below zero to freeze all that water.

Admittedly my experience with cold never did compare with the experience of polar explorers or others to whom sixty below zero might be commonplace; and I feel like a novice when I read of people enduring temperatures of a hundred below. That these people may have electrically heated garments and similarly modern comforts does not detract from the fact that they know an intensity of cold that I find difficult to imagine. I shall have to be satisfied with my memories of cold on a much more modest scale.

Nevertheless, the weather I knew when trapping in northern Minnesota in my late teens was cold. During three months of thickening ice and deepening snow, I do not recall having seen anything melt in the outside air without the warmth of body heat or fire. Temperatures got down to twenty to forty degrees below zero almost every night from late December until the first of the spring thaws. Twice I was told the minimal daily temperatures observed at Waskish on Upper Red Lake—thirty-three below on what felt like a slightly colder than ordinary day and forty-two below on a day that felt much colder. I spent the latter day cutting cordwood. My outer garments were frosted over like the fur on the horses pulling the bobsled. One other day felt so much colder than the day of forty-two below that I guessed it must have been about fifty-five below.

On another day when the temperature dropped down and down, maybe down to forty or fifty below zero or lower, I could not face the strong wind coming off the lake. I had to take off my snowshoes and walk backward across the mouth of the Tamarack River from the shelter of the woods to the Chippewa Trading Post at Waskish. (On another such day sixteen years later, some scientific colleagues of mine were traveling by dog team in the Big Bog at a temperature of fifty-two below zero; they barely made it to a patrol cabin and finished up by carrying the dogs.)

By early winter I was wearing four pairs of heavy woolen socks inside lumberjack style, leather-topped rubbers. If one sock had an unmended hole, a cold foot usually reminded me of it. When needing to do an open-air job with bare hands—such as tying the laces of snowshoe bindings—I would kneel, determine where to put my mittens so I could grab them in a hurry, jerk off the mittens and put them there, tie the laces before my fingers stiffened, and jam my hands back into the mittens. I did not do much shooting; when I did, it had to be without long aiming. Manipulating picture-wire rabbit snares had to be done as much as possible with mittens on. In cleaning game or skinning anything, I held the knife in a mittened hand after opening the blade very quickly with bare fingers. I did not clean or skin much in that cold—mostly an occasional porcupine for food; steaming warm tissue hardened as I looked at it, and bloody surfaces grew pale.

The cold had a bite that tightened the skin of my face and shot little pains like slight electric shocks through the sides of my nostrils as they hardened. Then I had to put up my mittened hand to keep the freezing from going deeper. When making a start on a trapline before sunrise and anticipating exceptional cold, I sometimes stuck fresh pieces of skin from a snowshoe hare, flesh side down, on my cheeks and sides of nose; these seemed to prevent the actual freezing of my face.

My snowshoes creaked on the packed trail. There might be a frozen weasel in a trap or a frozen snowshoe hare in a snare. Red squirrels would be out, and chickadees would flit and fluff and dee-dee. As the sun came up I might open my mackinaw or the collars of the two or three woolen shirts and the two suits of heavy woolen underwear that I wore. I might estimate that the temperature would be getting up to twenty below zero—maybe up to ten below.

During a period of intense cold the balance was so fine between comfort and discomfort that I seldom could stop to rest for more than a few minutes. At the same time I felt that I had to avoid sweating or breathing in the dangerous air too fast or too deeply. Now I suspect I may have overestimated the danger of freezing lungs.

I forgot to be careful about breathing on only the one occasion during the winter when I found anything alive in a trap or snare. A snowshoe hare was alive and uninjured in a snare, probably having run into it as I approached. It was lively and looked like an animal that might make a pet; so I held it between my knees, removed the noose from its neck, and used the wire to bind its hind legs together. All this I did with mittened hands, merely winding the untied snare wire around and around the captive's legs. A short distance farther along the snareline, a snare with slipped noose dangled over a runway. To have my hands free to adjust the noose I put my captive down in the snow. It started crawling off, ineffectually at first. The wire about its hind legs began to loosen, so I started after it—off through a dense stand of young jack pines. The hare stayed barely out of reach; I ran through the brush on snowshoes, breaking trail and running humped over to clear the boughs and branches overhead. Finally the hare kicked loose the rest of the binding, and away it went. I was panting, and my lungs were hurting. I was scared, and held my breath as long as I could and drew in what air I had to through my nostrils. The pain gradually subsided.

Incidentally, it was here near the far end of my snareline that I once found myself lost in an extensive block of forest. A light snow was falling. Even where I could look up through the trees at the sky, I could not see the sun. I did not realize that I was lost until I had walked for about an hour, heading in what I thought was the direction of the river. There had been nothing frightening about this experience—only annoyance—for I knew broadly where I was with respect to the river, and if necessary I could always backtrack. The psychologically odd thing to me was that I did not believe my compass and kept walking in the direction where I thought the river had to be rather than where the compass indicated. After another half-hour of this non-sense, I obeyed the compass and came out on the river some two miles upstream from where I expected to be.

When the snow became knee deep early in the winter, I invested three dollars in a pair of Indian-made snowshoes and rigged up bindings to fit leather-topped rubbers. Walking strad-dle-legged and with the unaccustomed weight on my feet, I quickly learned that I had some sets of muscles to train. It did not take long to gain proficiency with snowshoes, however, and I soon had trails packed for the length of my traplines and to all the places I visited regularly.

But travel with snowshoes was not as easy or convenient as unimpeded travel without them in the absence of snow. The webbing or frames sometimes caught on twigs, snowshoes sometimes entangled with each other, or something else hap-pened to plunge me into the snow—gun, packsack, and all. Once I lost my balance and fell while breaking a trail over very deep soft snow, and there I hung suspended upside down by the snowshoes without finding anything solid to get hold of from beneath until I could free my feet from the snowshoe bindings. Another time I was in no position to repair a snowshoe away from camp and learned the hard way what it was to wade, when already tired, through a couple of miles of deep soft snow. I carried both snowshoes on my shoulders and alternately pushed along and rested to recover breath for about three hours.

From the cabin I usually maintained two to four partially overlapping traplines, all in the form of loops that were up to ten miles in circumference. I covered each trapline about once a week. There was no chance of trap victims escaping or being left alive to suffer needlessly in the great cold, so I did not have to adhere to a regular schedule. Sometimes I covered one trapline in a morning and another in the afternoon. Sometimes I did not cover any trapline for a day or two. The most pressing day-by-day job was keeping enough firewood cut and ready for stuffing into the oil-barrel stove.

I had good mink trapping along the Tamarack River early in the winter, but after the weather became very cold the minks were not at all easy to catch. This was partly because of my relative inexperience as a trapper; I was not as clever at it as I might have been, not sufficiently discriminating to see which were the most promising trap sets. This was also partly because of the special wariness of some of the minks; they could detect carefully concealed traps almost regardless of what I did, even after a snowfall obliterated all signs of my having made the trap sets.

With the intensification of the cold, a weather-conscious mink might stick its head out of a hole in a beaver lodge or a stream-edge snowdrift. As the snow deepened, the minks did not come out at all. When I shoveled away snow with a snowshoe and chopped down through the ice in the right places, I saw that they were living below where the muskrats were. On splashed icy shelves were fish heads and scales, frog eggs, clamshells, blood, bits of vegetation, and sometimes remains of thin muskrats. Beneath the shelves dark passages led still farther out of sight. After I had done the digging and chopping, the minks would no longer use such a disturbed place.

Except for the snowshoe hares, the extremely abundant weasels were the principal animals to leave tracks over extensive surfaces of the snow from midwinter to the first of the spring thaws; and it was apparent the weasels were getting most of their living beneath the snow. The weasels were the most indefatigable runners all over the snow and tunnelers through it. Their trails would go bounding over meadows, swamps, stream edges, and through forests. When I found a hole in the snow with several weasel trails going in and out of it, I might dig down to see what could be found. Usually when I could trace a weasel's tunnel without snow falling into my digging and covering up everything, all I could find would be a hole leading into frozen ground. (Short-tailed shrews frequented the weasel holes; one of them hollowed out a trapped weasel, leaving the skin undamaged.) The snow-buried marshes and bogs and meadows always looked as though they belonged to the weasels.

I could not always do anything about some of the animals I especially coveted. Fisher tracks appeared at the far end of one of my traplines—great bounding trails in the powdery snow. The fishers were really worth money then, and I considered trying to track one down as the Indians were said to do; but I did not know how I could safely spend two or three days and nights on a fisher trail, camping outside in the forty-below-zero cold.

I have many memories of the snowshoe hares upon which I subsisted from preference as much as possible. Despite the disinclination of the hares to be active during daylight, their sign showed well what they did at night. They beat some most convenient trails for snare-setting through the thickets from one favored feeding ground to another. They ate on the twigs and smaller branches of the green aspens in the hardwood fringe along the river. Sometimes the hares left impressions of their sitting bodies in the alders or willows at the edge of the woods, though without tracking up open snow very much. They obviously did not like to get out in the open and seldom did anything so rash as running across the river. Before the winter was over, my snaring reduced the population of hares in the vicinity of the cabin to the point where the yield was no longer worth the effort snaring; I discontinued after I had snared about a hundred hares from the square mile most convenient for me to cover.

(A spectacular population peak had occurred seven or eight years before. Old-time trappers, lumbermen, and foresters had seen the woods south of the Tamarack River and east of Upper Red Lake swarming with the hares. One observer had even found them sitting in groups on snow-covered patches of the lake ice miles from shore. Estimates of hares in sight near shore ran as high as fifty per acre. The shore zone for miles had been littered with remains of hares estimated in the thousands—victims of weakness or of predatory birds gathered in the hardwoods along the banks. Great horned owls had been the most common predators in sight, but there were some snowy and great gray owls and several kinds of hawks as well. This movement across the lake had apparently been of short duration. Following it, hardly any live or healthy hares had remained in the area south of the Tamarack for the rest of the winter, and the period of extreme scarcity had continued at least through the next year.)

In the vastness and solitude of northern Minnesota's Big Bog, nothing fascinated me more than the timber wolves. At night, as the ice boomed and the tree trunks popped in the brittle air, a wolf howl carried well. The wolves were the freest of all the Big Bog animals that had to travel on four legs. Their power in bounding through deep snow seemed to me only less than the power of those immensely powerful snow travelers, the moose. Wolf packs might run on the ice fields of Upper Red Lake as they traveled between the chief deer yards south of the Tamarack River and the woodland caribou range far off to the west and northwest. Distances meant little to the wolves when they wanted to travel.

White cedar swamps were the winter retreats of the deer; one extensive deer yard lay not many miles from my cabin. On bright nights I could sometimes hear the howling of wolves as it came faintly from what I thought was this yard. Occasionally the howling might be quite plain.

I would prowl these places at night, crouching through thick clumps of spruce or cedar, breaking trail with snowshoes, trying to keep dislodged snow from falling in the collar of my mackinaw, looking backward to see if some of the heavier shadows had moved; but I doubt that I ever got very near the wolves trying to work up to them with my shotgun.

Or I might go to Waskish in an evening for mail and listen for wolf howls. I hoped that a wolf pack might follow me out of curiosity, with a nighttime tameness, and obligingly circle within range of buckshot loads. The idea of getting a hundred dollars in pelts and bounties with a few shots in an adventurous way appealed to me very much.

By midwinter I still had shot no wolves. I had not yet learned how to snare large animals. I could not afford any outlay of cash for wolf traps, and I was not sure I could catch wolves if I had traps. Therefore, I intensified my efforts to hunt them; whatever may be said of my methods, I tried.

With the flat-trajectory .250 rifle I would station myself early in the morning at a strategic lookout to wait for daybreak. After a series of terrifically cold mornings with no success, I finally gave up. Economically I did better trapping weasels at forty cents apiece and cutting cordwood at fifteen cents an hour for the box stove in the Chippewa Trading Post at Waskish.

I never did get any real timber wolves, that winter or any other. I did not even see any of the particular northern Minnesota wolves I had been trying to hunt. Still I had many opportunities to read the stories of their tracks. I saw where they seemed to frolic or otherwise enjoy themselves, behaving just like the natural wild dogs they were. They were most circumspect in their behavior toward me; the nearest they ever came was when three of them loped past the cabin one night on their way upriver.

If I wanted to do something different other than cover another trapline (particularly if the spare woodpile along one wall inside the cabin was reassuringly heaped nearly to the roof), I would head off deep into the Big Bog on snowshoes with some fried venison in a pocket and my gun to see what I could find. A little lake lay off by itself in some of the most beautiful surroundings in all the Big Bog country. Beside the lake stood an old cabin and in the cabin clearing the top of an ornately carved wooden cross stuck out of the snow. I never learned who lived and died there but thought that it must have been some Finn or Swede who chose to do so because it reminded him of some lonely setting of woods and waters in which he had lived before.

Along the shore of the lake I sometimes found wolf tracks— heavy trails partly filled in with drifted snow, tracks evenly spaced or in bounds. I remember wolf trails going past a partly fallen log barn and walking tracks around one corner of the barn. I cannot be sure that the wolves used the corner of the barn as a scent station, but I think they did.

The sand ridges covered with virgin timber that protruded here and there from the surrounding bog lands were delightful places to explore. Red squirrels dominated the ridges, though weasels and foxes tracked up the snow there too. The squirrels worked over the snow and dug for buried things; they ran through the pines, fed on cones, and sat and barked. Wolves had been around earlier, and I was convinced that those ridges had meant something special to them during the warmer seasons, offering some of the driest and most secluded den sites in the Big Bog.

My very gradual maturing did not lead to exclusively serious thoughts or behavior. I remember with satisfaction some nonsense involving a red squirrel on my northern Minnesota trapline. This squirrel was nearly always at its station in a big Norway pine, from which it would address me in the most scolding tone as I traveled my snowshoe trail below. I came to anticipate my scolding and was glad the squirrel was there to give it to me, yet I felt a peculiar malice toward it. One day the squirrel was in a little pine tree out of jumping distance from any other tree, and I ran up to see what might be done. The squirrel clung to the top of the little tree, notably subdued. I found that I could move the treetop, in a wider arc with each push and pull, until the squirrel was waving back and forth from the top like a pennant, hanging on by its front feet. The squirrel finally shook loose, dropped into the snow, bounded to the big pine, and ran up to its customary perch at the base of a limb.

I do not think I have ever seen any nonhuman creature so enraged as that squirrel. It jumped up and down on its perch, choked and sputtered, and burst into the nearest equivalent of a sustained roar of which a red squirrel would seem capable. Thereafter it would start scolding at me well before I appeared in sight of the big pine, and it would still be scolding as long as I remained within hearing distance.

As I think about the camp on the Tamarack River, I find memories of the camp and of its surroundings rather inseparable.

Porcupines added variety not only to my diet but also to the cabin's surroundings. My first glimpse of one against a background of sky and dark greenery behind the cabin suggested a small bear, as did its heavy flat-footed trail in the snow. But in their gnawing away at raw patches of bark of upper limbs and trunks and in their prickly displays while bunched up and alarmed, the porcupines revealed themselves as most peculiar animals adapted to live when and how they did. Their quills had a menacing fascination for me—especially the quills on that awful weapon, the tail—as they parted in masses to display their whole white shafts. Somehow nearly every time I skinned a porcupine I got a few of the quills in my woolen outdoor clothing which worked through and reminded me later of porcupine.

On the cabin roof and round the garbage heap, chickadees and Canada jays sat and flew and searched and pecked. Sometimes in the night I heard the hooting of horned owls. One of them gave me some competition for the local snowshoe hares early in the winter.

One of the little nostalgic fragments that stays with me relates to a creature of the wilderness that established its headquarters in the cabin with me. I had heard the whistling and rustling of a mouse for several evenings. Then one morning as I tried to put on a leather-topped rubber, I discovered a cache of prune pits. In evenings as I lay on the bed finishing supper dessert, I tossed prune pits into the woodpile corner from where the sounds came. Gradually I began tossing pits along the wall, nearer and nearer to me. The mouse worked nearer and nearer to the light, gathering the pits, until I could see that it was a deer mouse. I could see its white underparts and watch its squirrellike foraging before it went scampering off into the darkness with another pit.

The exploitation of furbearers—my economic justification for wintering in northern Minnesota's Big Bog—turned out to have almost minor importance, though it took a great amount of time and effort. I worked hard at the trapping, from which my returns in cash were modest indeed. Mostly I caught weasels, along with some minks. For a seven-month stay I did little better than make expenses, with much living off the country and a good deal of doing without things that cost money—the same as everyone did up there.

By the time the five feet of snow was reduced to slush and mud but before the spring breakup and the opening of the ice on the lakes, I loaded my canoe, camping equipment, traps, gun, and everything I wanted to take with me onto a bobsled and rode to the railroad town of Kelliher. I had already disposed of my fur.

For the most part, memories are what the Big Bog paid off in: memories of northern terrain, of cold, of deep-snow traplines, of wilderness wild creatures—whether a squalling lynx or a white-footed mouse that cached prune pits in my footwear.

T WAS THE FIRST OF JUNE, AND THE TWICE-A-week train—consisting of steam engine and ca-boose—bumped and rocked along on not much more than a corduroy road. Within the caboose, with my canoe and camping equipment, I was go-ing to International Falls. From there I would travel across the border and on up into the great wilderness of northern Ontario. This was what I had been working toward and saving my money for.

My cash resources back then in the early nineteen twenties totaled about five hundred dollars—trapline dollars, axe-work dollars, savings from hard, ten-hour-day labor with hoes, shovels, pitchforks, crowbars, wheelbarrows. I had a high school diploma, and I was also, at nineteen, something of a vet-eran hunter and trapper, having started hunting and trapping as a serious business at the beginning of my teens. The pre-vious fall and winter had given me seven months of hunting and trapping in northern Minnesota's Big Bog country, northeastward from Upper Red Lake.

I wanted to be a naturalist, and a youngster who wanted to be a naturalist in the early part of the twentieth century had a very limited choice in ways of making a living. The sole profes-sional opportunity that I could see for becoming a naturalist lay in a life at least partly dependent upon hunting and trapping.

Furthermore, I liked the freedom of a hunter and trapper's life in the wild out-of-doors—the freedom that was still possible then. I wanted to hunt and trap and live off the land, to breathe clean air and to enjoy the beauties of frost and sun dogs and landscapes having naturalness left in them. Without having any desire to be any sort of recluse—I liked solitude as long as I did not get too much of it—I could endure loneliness when need-ing to and took pride in being a wilderness man or, at any rate, in having a start on being a wilderness man.

Also, I can confess to a romanticism that gave me a liking

for the physical dangers of a wilderness life. I would talk down the dangers to my worrying mother, but I knew that they existed. I knew the danger in a glancing axe blade but felt confident in retaining some control of the axe even when it glanced, and I liked to talk about it to people other than my mother. I liked to talk about the danger of going through thin or rotten ice, about the mishaps that could befall one out there all alone, about storms and hardships.

But I never did anything I considered really foolhardy—I just had a taste for chance taking that might come close to the edge.

Firearms I treated with great respect.

Enroute to International Falls, I looked from the caboose windows at the settlers' clearings and the few small towns with frame and log buildings that we passed through. On snowshoes, I had gotten into some of this same country near the railroad the winter before, but my trapping headquarters had been many miles from any railroad and many miles from what could have been called much of an automobile road. It had been more in backwoods than in wilderness, but some of the spaces where nobody lived had been extensive. I had seen areas having no visible trace of people, conceivably areas in which no other white man had ever been. Although it had been no wilderness comparable to what I was heading for on past International Falls, the Big Bog had, I felt, given me in seven months an introduction to a North Woods type of wilderness, a minimum of apprenticeship for the Canadian North.

The winter before, Big Bog temperatures had gotten down below forty degrees below zero, and snow had accumulated in depths up to five feet on the level. Northern Ontario surely could not beat that kind of winter very much. In the Big Bog I had been accustomed to covering a trapline during the daylight hours and then, if I wanted to, prowling most of the night seeking an adventure with wolves. I felt that I had all of the durability that northern Ontario would require of me.

The lumbering industry dominated the economy of the area I rode through on the way to International Falls. Through the caboose windows I looked at horses and teamsters, at sawmills, piles of cut lumber, loaded flatcars on sidings, storekeepers, people standing around station platforms. At International Falls there were the largest piles of logs—spruce pulpwood—that I ever saw. Spread-out waters at the mouth of Rainy River were covered by rafts of logs.

The view was northern but not northern enough to suit me.

Soon after entering Canada at Fort Frances from International Falls, I came up against a dismaying reality. I could not attain the requisite legal status to obtain resident hunting and trapping licenses before winter began, and I did not have anywhere nearly sufficient money to pay nonresident fees and still buy a winter's provisions. If I were to winter in any remote wilderness, I would have to reach it and be established well before freeze-up in a snug camp, with plenty of provisions and game cached, plenty of wood cut, and a working familiarity with my hunting and trapping territory.

The Royal North West Mounted Police suggested that I might work at a job somewhere until I qualified as a resident. Or, without any licenses, or with only a fishing license, I might look over the country, asking advice at Hudson's Bay Company and RNWMP posts. The police advised me to take along enough to eat and watch out for dangerous waters.

The police were nice to me, and I left their office at Fort Frances feeling grateful and at the same time with certain underlying doubts. I had a disquieting feeling that my Big Bog experience might not be adequate preparation for what I was planning to do.

The area that interested me above all others was known as Patricia. I had read that this was as wild as any region of Canada and that it had lots of game and fur. From descriptions, I believed it the ideal objective for one of my tastes. The prospect of going to it was nothing less than enchanting. And on the map it looked more accessible than many other attractive blank spaces in the Canadian North.

I did not know exactly how to reach it but reasoned that I could follow main water courses and work along the side of James Bay. Nothing about this promised to be easy, but such a travel route might be possible.

For the first exploration trip, the best bet seemed to be to travel by train to Longlac, thence by canoe down the Kenogami River. The name Mammamattewa on the map might indicate a place worth heading for as a preliminary try.

The view from the train illustrated what maps did not

show. A vast wilderness burn—vast even in terms of Canadian vastness—was the landscape I watched for hours. Bare rock and charred tree trunks. There were more hours of a continuous succession of little lakes bounded by spruce-covered rocky hills. North of Lake Superior almost every stream seemed to be a cascade half-choked with dead trees.

How did one travel by canoe in a place like that? Maybe one did not.

After unloading at Longlac and making camp near the railroad station for the coming night, I paddled over to a Hudson's Bay Company store that I could see on the other side of a lake. The waves were running three feet high but without whitecaps. Riding the troughs, I could manage the nearly empty canoe and still feel daring. The crossing gave me a workout and took out of me the stuffiness of the railroad travel.

In the morning, as I was rolling up the cruiser tent, the stationmaster came to ask if I wished to go with two Indians who were then starting for the town of Grant, which was about forty miles to the northeast. I did wish to, and I got my light-travel outfit into the canoe just in time.

One of the Indians was a young man who spoke no English and paid no attention to me, but the older man was affable. As we paddled side by side, I asked the old Indian questions, and when I ran out of questions, he did the talking. He said that he was seventy-five years old, that he had served in France during the war, and that he had lied about his age to get into the army.

His age was a joke to him. The recruiting people had not been particular about such things as long as a man could take care of himself. The old man could take care of himself. Despite a face about as wrinkled as even Indian faces get to be, he had strength and endurance left. At the beginning of a portage I saw him heave onto his back and walk away with a pack the weight of which I estimated at two hundred pounds.

He thought that I did pretty well, paddling alone, to keep up with them, paddling double. I was not overpaced in the actual paddling, but when I had to make two trips to a portage—one carrying the canoe and another carrying the packsack, cruiser tent, and bedding—to the Indians' one trip, I had to work to catch up again when back on the water. When the Indians stopped for tea in the middle of the morning, I thought that I had better go on ahead of them and make up in advance some of the time lost on my two-trip portages. The old man told me to run the next two rapids and then portage around the third.

I ran one rapid, but, when I came to what I counted as the second rapid, it did not look right to me. I worked over toward the shore to be in a better position to get out of the current if I had to. The current helped—it took the canoe over to the shore and held it tight against the bank in a sparse willow thicket.

There I sat, looking at a rapid and thinking that the roar I was hearing must be from the rapid farther ahead that I was not to run. Still, I could see no inviting channel to run in the rapid directly ahead of me. I was sitting in the canoe trying to make up my mind where to run that rapid when the Indians came packing along the shore.

The old man asked me sharply what I was doing there. I replied that I was looking, got out, and started portaging.

In portaging around, I could see that there were no stopping places between the upper part and the roaring waters downstream. The Kenogami at that place was constricted into a long series of rapids, cascades, and falls, with great rocks and pouring water that no man could have expected to live through once he got into it.

The sight of it left me benumbed and with no immediate inclination to be reflective in detail.

I remember another portage along the Kenogami. The trail of generations of portagers was worn hip deep through the peaty accumulations of the forest floor, and in the places having firm mud in the trail were footprints of moose and wolves among the human tracks. In other places, the trail led over high rocks overlooking the white water of the river. Rocks and tree roots and fallen tree trunks had to be stepped over or gone around. Some of the rocky ledges over which the trail led were wet and slippery from the spray. I might have to steady myself by grabbing a limb or small tree trunk with one hand while hanging onto the canoe with the other hand.

Because of a slight leakiness, my eighteen-foot, canvas-covered canoe took up considerable water on that first day out, and, together with a carrying yoke hastily improvised from poles, it must have weighed substantially over one hundred pounds. I weighed one hundred forty, and on the longer portages would be panting, and my legs would be wobbling after the first quarter to half of a mile. It was, nevertheless, easier to keep panting and wobbling to the end of a long portage than to try to break up a carry with rests.

94

In one instance, after leaving the Kenogami to take a more cross-country route, I finished a portage having an estimated length of two miles, put down the canoe, and paddled across a narrow lake, only to find myself confronted by another long portage. My fatigue was so great from the portage just covered that I had a hard time getting the canoe back on my shoulders. When I got under way once more, I somehow staggered through this portage, too.

On the water again, however, I recovered quickly, but the Indians were so far ahead of me that I could no longer see them and had to do my own finding of portage trails. I had misgivings about this, for the trails were simply unmarked utility trails for northerners, never meant for tourists. I knew, broadly, the direction that the route had to take, sooner or later found what I had to find, and ultimately caught up with the Indians at another teatime.

My impression was that I portaged about ten miles on that one day, but ten miles was undoubtedly an overestimation. Such distances could be easy to overestimate by a youngster carrying the loads that I had. But even were my estimate to be halved, I still saw as much of portage trails from under a waterlogged canoe as I wanted to.

Along in the evening, while still a couple of hours short of Grant, we made camp, and I invited the Indians to share my cruiser tent with me behind mosquito netting. This made a full cruiser tent, with two big Indians and me, but the mosquitoes of the darkness outside were becoming so savage the old Indian admitted he was glad to be inside.

We got along all right, and soon I was aware of daybreak.

Then, a splashing outside, and the old Indian made a low exclamation that I did not understand. He opened the mosquito netting and crawled out. There were three heavy, hanging reports, the sound of a body falling in water, some more splashing. I followed the young Indian out of the tent.

A yearling moose floated at the edge of the lake, about fifty feet away, and the old Indian was putting down a .38–.40 carbine. The Indians had needed dog food, and here it was. I built a fire while the Indians took a canoe to go out and do the butchering. Butchering under the circumstances was cutting off the hind legs, which had the meat concentrated in the most readily transportable form.

The morning mist cleared away from the woods and rocks

and spruce-covered hills. The new day turned out to be still and hot. The Indians could not travel as fast with the moose meat as they had without it, and I had time to do some looking down through water at fishes lying deep below the surface. Water beetles traced endlessly back and forth. The sun grew hotter over the quiet water.

I would pick out targets for the bow of the canoe, and with a quick stroke terminated by a flip of the paddle would center the bow over a lily pad or run the bow between a pair of rush stems protruding out of the water. I would make little whirlpools with paddle strokes and watch the canoe glide as it left them behind.

All of us seemed to be getting somewhat lazy. The Indians had to stop for another tea before we reached Grant, toward the middle of the morning.

It took me until about the middle of June to acknowledge to myself that I did not have the means of doing in that year what I had come up into the wilderness to do—to live as a trapper. Meanwhile, I had seen a considerable portion of the Canadian North.

There had been more, much more, of the rock faces, burns, forests and wetlands, turbulent rivers, and names on maps that were names only of post offices. It was all the real North, and, at one pulpwood town where I stayed a night and most of a day, the people were so friendly that I was tempted to take a job there, but working at a lumber mill was still not what I had come up to do.

About then I acknowledged another reality: I should do some more growing up before tackling, alone, a remote wilderness in the Canadian North.

I already had strength and toughness and stamina. I could endure hunger if I had to and could digest anything. I could sleep anywhere. When blackfly bites itched, I let them itch. I seemed able to keep my head in emergencies that progressed to the point of being recognizable emergencies.

Still, I needed more years. The idea did not please me, for I had long been touchy about my elders regarding me as just a kid and telling me that I needed years more than anything else.

I doubt if I would have admitted it out loud, but I had come to see that, in my case, there was no substitute for the years themselves in the process of growing up to be a man who could take care of himself wherever he went.

My mistaken judgment upstream from that rapid had been the one thing to bring me around to put it frankly to myself that the Canadian wilderness North was too dangerous for me at that stage of my development. I had probably been my closest to death right then, and if I argued that the fault had not been mine, that I had gotten there through doing only what the Indian had told me to do, the unreassuring truth remained that I had not recognized a deadly danger. Veteran woodsman that I could consider myself to be, lack of years and the discretion of years could still betray me on a matter concerning which there could be no chance to try again and do better next time.

However gradually my attitude toward the romance of danger may have been changing in the process of my growing up, the experience of the rapid led to some sobering meditation. In that connection, among others, I was no longer disposed to maintain—as I frequently had earlier—that my life was mine, that if I got killed, it would be nobody's business except my own.

Others did have some rights in me. I recalled my return after the winter in the Big Bog, when my mother had exclaimed, "You are actually home!"—as if she had never expected to see me again. There had been the many nonrelatives who had put something in me, from small kindnesses to a great deal beyond anything their possible responsibilities toward me could have called for. For example, teachers, at the cost of inconvenience and extra work for themselves, had from time to time permitted me to stay out of school to trap and to make up my studies later—or to make up my studies in advance. They had actively encouraged me in my efforts to become a naturalist. They had talked with me in evenings. None of these people had made their personal investments in me so that I could waste my life dying in a rapid—or from starvation or in a tundra blizzard or in some other way before I was old enough to know better.

In my psychological metamorphosis at nineteen, I found myself coming up to another realization. Perhaps I should say that about this time, along with my developing views about the wrongness of taking unnecessary chances, I began to regard unnecessary chance taking as professionally unbefitting.

I was ashamed of the affair of the rapid. It had betrayed dubbishness of a sort that I could not excuse in myself—dubbishness that I should not have expected in an older, more mature man, even a man who had never seen a rapid before. Only a dub, I knew, took unnecessary chances in things that really counted.

The Canadian wilderness had neither an inimical nor a friendly aspect—only, out there in the vastnesses where no people lived, an impersonality and an unfeelingness that I often compared with interstellar space. If anything was there that could live, it lived; if it could not live, it did not.

Without my knowing the ecology of northern wildernesses as well as I would later, the impressions I had at nineteen as to enormous tracts being without much that a man could live on were, in the main, correct. A wilderness need not be full of game and fur merely because it is empty of people. The Canadian North could have its own kinds of emptiness in somewhat the same sense as a mountain could have its emptiness at timberline or higher. There could be expanses of not much more than water and rock, or of not much more than water, rock, bog, and forest, without much animal life except in special places.

In the special places there might be trout, pike, moose, caribou, muskrats, grouse, squirrels, foxes, beavers, ducks, and hares living in abundance—though even the special places did not always have their abundances of animal life.

I knew where I would stand in that wilderness. I would live or die on the same terms as did the Indians, the wolves, the hares, the grouse, the chickadees, and the rest, living if I could and dying if I had to. I had better be using my head in what I did up there.

So I went back home to grow up some more.

In going back home I was not giving up the Canadian North. I never did get to Patricia and never became a Canadian trapper, but I lived and traveled in or close to other Canadian wildernesses and northern wildernesses elsewhere—this after I had gained more understanding and expertness by first doing more living under conditions that allowed more leeway for the mistakes of inexperience.

The northern wilderness was beautiful, as the stars were beautiful. The northern wilderness offered no personal challenge to anyone except insofar as a person chose to make a challenge out of the fact that it was there. It was there, as were the stars, in magnificent impersonality.

In my scientific work, I saw more northern wilderness during my forties and fifties than during my teens and twenties, and some of it was in the Canadian North. I saw it traveling by auto, aircraft, and freight canoe as well as by paddling canoe and by foot trail.

I cannot say that all of this made me feel young again, for the travel had serious purposes, some of which I could not even have guessed in my earlier years; but once in a while I might have the feeling of almost being swept back into the years, of almost imagining myself a trapper again.

I might feel this way especially while comparing trapping tricks with an Indian in the Saskatchewan Delta or while eating a meal with some old-timer in a patrol cabin, away up somewhere beyond roads and railroads. When one old-timer told me of seeing seven otters in a single day on a canoe trip in my youthful dreamland of Patricia, I prickled all over at the thought of it.

Even in middle age, I dream of the District of Patricia where I have never been but I always know when I am there. There are the minor variations, but the essential patterns keep coming out so much the same way, in dreams that tend to recur about every year or so. I am young and jog along game trails by the hour without tiring, through the pine and spruce and white cedar, through the birch and aspen, over the rocks and around the edges of lakes. There is mist over the lily ponds where the moose feed; the rapids roar, and the water lies glassy in the quiet places; and neither mosquitoes nor flies bite, nor are any problems vexatious.

Or the full moon lights the snow and streaks it with shadows, while the wolves howl in the distance, and I feel like answering them and running on through the night, being a part of it all.

Of Wilderness and Wolves

LDO LEOPOLD INTRODUCED ONE OF HIS essays with advice never to revisit a wilderness. Returning to a place of favorite memories after long absence would be likely not only to disappoint but also to tarnish the memories. I did not challenge the melancholy appropriateness of this advice in returning very purposefully to northern Minnesota's Big Bog area where I had lived as a fur trapper twenty-eight years before. I knew that I would find changes that quite possibly might not please me.

Twenty-eight years after my winter in the Big Bog, Waskish was a small town with a U.S. highway passing through it. A highway bridge crossed the mouth of the Tamarack River. The downstream river banks were lined with summer cottages.

During the period between my wintering and return, all physical traces of my having lived there—that I could recognize—had disappeared. I could not find so much as one of my cut stumps at my former cabin site a few miles upstream from Waskish, and the cabin was gone. My old winter headquarters may be said to exist only in memory, along with many other things antedating the summer cottages and the highway.

The Big Bog was no longer subject to the human exploitation and the promotional schemes of earlier in the century. In the midthirties, the federal government had resettled most of the remaining farmers in places where they would have a better chance to make a living. After its withdrawal from agricultural use, it had been managed by public agencies as wild land for game production, hunting, and related purposes for which it was adapted. As a wilderness, the Big Bog was not, in the late forties, anything much resembling the wilderness that the white man had found there; but it had regained some of the wilderness features lost during the boom period of human set-

Living Wilderness 33(107): 3–7 (1969) and 34(112): 49–51 (1970–1971).

tlement. Perhaps it might be considered, battered as it was, a triumphant wilderness insofar as its human invaders had essentially withdrawn—that is, away from the highway, the summer cottages, and a few roads leading into one place or another.

An inland post office had become during the twenty-eight years a "ghost" of fallen, rotten logs. I did not find much left of the stands of pines, nor of the hardwood fringes along the Tamarack River, nor anything of the once-extensive white cedar swamps. The savannah was enlarged and the swamps and bogs less diversified and more open, similar in appearance to the vast Canadian wetlands hundreds of miles to the northwest. As before, the ditches had beavers, and probably more beavers than before. As before, a sand ridge along the north shore of Upper Red Lake was covered with a mixture of hardwood trees and berry bushes.

The last of the woodland caribou up there in the expanses of the bog and swamp north of the lake had gone, though not before great effort had been made by conservation agencies to save them. Those caribou had been the last free-living remnant of the species south of the Canadian border. To the dwindling stock had been added animals live-trapped in Canada. They had gone, too. The edge of a species' range had ceased to be range at all.

Some people blamed the wolves for the loss of the woodland caribou, and the wolves were known to have killed caribou, but the explanation is unlikely to be anything so simple and direct when a population disappears from an outskirt of its native range. Indian hunting could have been more than the fading species could withstand, but that explanation does not take us far into fundamentals either. Neither wolves nor Indians explain the dwindling that had earlier gone on. Local extinction had been the culminating symptom of a biological impossibility. When I first knew that country, the caribou had probably been more abundant than the moose in the wildest parts of the Big Bog. As the caribou had faded, the moose had increased, and neither wolves nor Indians nor fires nor plant succession had prevented the increase of the moose. Moose country it had become, the moose belonged there, and the moose were there to prove it.

Other age-tested natives were there along with the moose and the wolves, wherever they belonged: the deer, the ruffed

101

grouse and sharp-tailed grouse, the skunks and weasels and foxes, the snowshoe hares.

It was a quiet, sunny day of early fall when I walked along the north shore sand ridge of Upper Red Lake on the occasion of my return to the Big Bog country. The deciduous leaves were coloring, and the mosquitoes had given up. A bald eagle was flying overhead. I felt at the same time a great peace and a great longing.

I still wanted what my middle age had in family satisfactions; but I longed to be young, with youthful stamina and lack of big responsibilities, to be living in an interlude again, as a predator in wilderness solitudes, yet not so far into solitudes as to be out of reach of companionship when companionship was needed.

Walking along the lake beach, I pulled apart a wolf dropping containing the remains of snowshoe hare. The wolf sign more than anything else aroused memories of a part of the world as it once had been compared with what it had become. This, more than anything else, was assurance that the Big Bog was still wilderness, despite the decades of human abuse and the new cottages along the Tamarack. "Wolf country" this had been since before the white man came, and "wolf country" it still was.

Farther north into Canada, the wildernesses that I know are wolf wildernesses. In these wildernesses, the wolves may not be the least obtrusive. One may, while traveling, think of wolves only now and then and not with any sense of their really dominating anything. To me, they fit into the northern wilderness scene across the border north from Upper Red Lake and Lake of the Woods as salt fits into a recipe, unobtrusively yet part of it.

When the wolves are there, one can see the sign. A portage trail that is not too exclusively packed with human tracks may show some wolf tracks. Game trails have wolf tracks among the moose tracks and rabbit tracks and the tracks of the other wild creatures that naturally use game trails. Wolf and moose or deer tracks show on river banks and mud bars and lake edges. Weathered wolf droppings may be found if one looks in the right places. Or one may not actually look to find the droppings— they may just be there in plain sight, with the old deer hair or rabbit fur or feather butts sticking out of the claylike body of a dropping. If a big carcass lies in some conspicuous place, maybe it will show tooth marks of wolves; but except under certain circumstances, one is unlikely to find many carcasses, at any rate without looking for them and knowing where to look. The wolf sign is more likely to be tracks in places wolves frequent in their ordinary business of being wolves.

A hotel lobby may have walls decorated with wolf skins. A rustic bedroom may have wolf rugs on the floor. Among the old family hand-downs may be wolf coats or wolf rugs.

That wolf-country wilderness is vast, though I do not know exactly how vast from personal experience. I have seen it by air from commercial planes for hours at a time. Extending westward, northward, and eastward from the The Pas, it looked all but endless—the lakes, marshes, swamps, bogs, the flat and the rough lands, the dense and the thin stands of trees and shrubs, the burned and the unburned, the expanses of what the Canadians call "the bush."

At low flying altitudes, the game trails were plainly visible wherever they were not overgrown by vegetation. The veteran northerner, Tom Lamb, flew me so low that I could look for muskrat cuttings and feeding platforms. In what was still woodland caribou range of central Saskatchewan, a lot of bog and open tamarack and spruce swamp and patches of higher ground looked to me very much as the woodland caribou range of northern Minnesota's Big Bog had looked when it had had caribou. Making allowance for the difference in detail to be seen from skimming past in a light plane in summer and breaking trail with snowshoes, I could sense rather than explain why the Big Bog had the last of Minnesota's woodland caribou and why central Saskatchewan still has the species.

Neither place was beautiful according to the usual standards of scenic grandeur. They both had their solitudes. The Big Bog, itself, had its thousands and thousands of acres where people seldom if ever went. It had wilderness where people did not live, possibly never have been, maybe not even Indians.

My criteria of wilderness values are put forth only as my own, and I do not suppose I can wholly define them. In part, wilderness values as I know them are those of naturalness, of cleanness and freedom. They afford a measure of peace to people whose tastes are like mine. They mean enough to cause some of us to fight for the preservation of wildernesses that we have neither seen nor expect to see. To those of us who see symptoms of biological and social unbalance in mankind's exploiting and defiling almost every place within reach, the preservation of wildernesses anywhere is a source of comfort.

The quality of naturalness in a wilderness has its relative aspects and its anthropocentric definitions. We may quibble over what constitutes naturalness and, of course, maintain that anything is natural, including all of man's activities. For the sake of conveying a thought, let it be said that naturalness in the way that I mean reflects the working of what we call Nature in contradistinction to the working of man.

In a "North Woods" wilderness there may be species that are beautiful according to nearly any human standard; others may be thought of as nothing special to look at, but still they belong. If the timber wolf were not beautiful, I would say it still would have its place as a wilderness animal, but I think it is very beautiful. I think it is as beautiful as anything it preys upon. Its beauty is that of power and ruggedness and movement, of the near perfection of a natural type. It is adjusted to its way of life, a natural creature uncorrupted by human tampering. It is beautiful in the sense that a goshawk, gyrfalcon, muskellunge, canvasback duck, or an otter may be beautiful.

The sleekest, most superb, full-sized timber wolves I ever saw were some snared in northern Minnesota. I cannot see any reasons other than fear, hate, jealousy, or misunderstanding why man should not appreciate the beauty of such as these. Theirs was the beauty of champions, if there ever were champions in anything, with heads that looked about a foot in width and powerful enough to bite a chunk out of any animal that they could take hold of, with necks, shoulders, and forelegs to match the heads. Surely they were a tested product of much evolution, whether to be regarded as an enemy of man or not. Northern winters, with their periods of famine and great cold, have, moreover, molded in the timber wolf a species endowed with qualities other than crude strength and stamina.

While I learned long ago that there are people interested in northern wildernesses who do not agree with me as to how much wolves belong in a wilderness scene, I am certain that my views are shared by others. Such practical men as Ira Gabrielson and Stanley Young, with their great experience in predator control programs, cannot fairly be charged with being overly sentimental in behalf of wolves; yet they have expressed hope that the remnant populations of timber wolves found in the northern Lake States will not be exterminated. These men, among other naturalists, have suggested that for biological and esthetic reasons preserves be dedicated to the wolves or the wolves be permitted to live unmolested in areas where their activities would not be in serious conflict with human interests.

The remaining wolves in the Upper Peninsula of Michigan and in northern Wisconsin are remnants, indeed. They are dangerously close to being lost as a species to those states. Perhaps they could not be saved on the Michigan and Wisconsin mainlands even if the public were to show far greater interest in saving them than it has shown to date. Northern Minnesota has its relatively strong stock of wolves to a large extent in spite of the public's animosity. The wolves are still killed by almost anyone having opportunity.

While I would not contend that there are any regions in the United States where free-living wolves should be given complete legal protection at all times, without any exceptions, it does not follow that wolves must be unremittingly campaigned against merely because it may be legal to do so. There remains the need for judgment, for rational policies and action.

The idea of a preserve for what Gabrielson referred to as "these magnificent predators" may be acceptable to many people in the abstract, but when it comes to planning for a preserve of this type, all kinds of objections have ways of arising. Even though viewed without hatred as wonderful animals and a priceless part of a wilderness heritage, even if one's sympathies are for the wolves, realities of damage resulting from wolves must still be considered.

A fair and workable zoning policy or system of indemnity for bona fide wolf damage might be prerequisite to the establishment of any real wilderness-and-wolf preserve. Attempting to keep the wolves and other wilderness predators killed off at public expense in order that someone may try to raise a few sheep in out-of-the-way places in nonagricultural country can be fully as absurd as would be the opposite extreme of tolerating the wolves where they would have real potentialities for damage to a sound stock-raising industry.

I do not recall having heard of wolves destroying livestock about the periphery of the Big Bog, though they surely must have done so. Even in recent times, publicized wolf damage to livestock has occurred as far south as central Minnesota, much outside of any consistently occupied timber wolf range. The possibility of—especially—unsophisticated young wolves straying into farming communities must be considered as part of reality. However, I have been informed by predator-control people that such stray wolves are relatively easy to eliminate.

The Big Bog *might* be one of the areas in northern United States where free-living timber wolves might be left in comparative peace. Perhaps it is not; perhaps there are good reasons why not. If not, if this is just one more of the places where human interests and wolves are incompatible, if the wolves really must be kept down to the lowest possible level, I would not advocate anything to the contrary.

At the same time, if man—without really valid justification—succeeds in making and keeping the Big Bog wolfless, by so much, in my opinion, shall he make this man-ravaged wilderness more nearly the worthless wasteland some people call it.

That the great values of our natural out-of-doors may be recreational is something I am willing to concede for the time being, from man-centered criteria and up to a point. I do not concede that recreational values must be primarily something to hunt or fish or even to visit at first hand. There are other matters of definition that I am not willing to concede, either; and I do not want to be pinned down too closely concerning some things that I know "by feel" more than by reasoned analyses.

My view has been—and still is—that civilized man should exploit only game species that are well enough situated to withstand a reasonable amount of exploitation. When I was young, waterfowl and prairie grouse were so abundant where I lived, so secure in their excellent habitats, and so little hunted by man, that gun pressure did not constitute the problem in their management that it now does. Today, in addition to the hoofed game that may be in many places far too abundant for its own good, the introduced ring-necked pleasant occurs by the millions where living conditions favor it in agricultural United States. In fact, numerous wild species are now available for orderly harvesting on a scale that would have been unimaginable during my youth; and I see nothing wrong about our taking advantage of these thriving or even overabundant wild species to the extent that exploitation of them is properly conducted.

Up to a certain point, unselfish motivations in conservation may hardly be dissociated from the selfish. I do not know when I became more concerned about what natural values posterity would have left than about what remained for me during my lifetime. But I do want posterity to have, and to continue having, opportunities for wholesome outdoor enjoyments such as I had when I was young.

In considering my own sentiments toward wildernesses and their creatures, I cannot underrate the motivations and trophy value of memories. In my case, memories comprise a big part of what I feel that I got out of my early life as a hunter and trapper. To a considerable extent they remain a part of my day-by-day living. At any rate, the places that I like best wherever I may be include those reminding me of the places that I knew in my early years—that is, the wilderness, and the wilder places of backwoods, prairie marshes and prairie streams, and the rugged country and great expanses of the high plains.

There is carryover from youth in my regrets that the larger wolves had to be extirpated over such a tremendous proportion—nearly all—of the range they once held in those parts of the United States lying south of the Canadian border. The distinctive quality that wolves impart to the memories of my younger years leaves me with a special awareness of how superbly they represent wilderness. There is carryover in my wanting to protect the remnant populations that persist in wilderness tracts where they neither do nor are likely to do much of anything detrimental to man.

My outdoor philosophies had not emerged in any clear, consistent, or final form after my earlier contacts with wildernesses. I probably recognized first the preciousness of solitude as an antidote to the overwhelming dominance of man. In addition, I should say that what has counted most to me in wilderness values has been the relative completeness of the living and nonliving constituents of a given tract of wilderness. I do not want to see even my favorites among plant and animal life living just anywhere—only where they belong, marsh and bog life in marshes and bogs, plains life on the plains, desert life in deserts, and so on, according to what is appropriate in natural biological equations.

107

As a conservationist, I have been disappointed in the losses of outdoor values that have occurred since my youth. The peace of mind that the out-of-doors has meant for me has often been offset by the wastage of woodlands, wetlands, and grasslands. I may wonder if mankind's overrunning and despoliation of the Earth will stop short of ruin of the values that go so far in making life worth living for people who now and then need solitude or natural wildness to remind them of something other than man. For there are those who maintain that the Earth will ultimately be so full of people that they will have to use everything for subsistence. There are even those who maintain that such is not only inevitable but desirable. There are certainly people to whom loss of outdoor values is no loss that they feel at all. National parks have lumber or other exploitable features that someone wants, and in almost unlimited variety, someone is always seeking economic gain at the expense of what is left in the natural out-of-doors.

When I have something like this to brood about, I may doubt that the interests that grew to be such a big part of my life since boyhood are anything to recommend for others. Then the mood passes, and I know that modern civilization is not exclusively moneymaking and gadgetry. An increasing number of articulate and determined people, like the late Bernard DeVoto, have been seeing something very wrong indeed about having to drive a hundred miles or more from home to reach a "reasonably neglected natural area." As has happened many times in recent years, it is heartening to have demonstrated that influential groups of people can, in the words of Ernest Swift, "refuse to swap a clear-running stream, a National Monument, public rights or a wilderness area for a fast and slippery buck." There is more behind the growing power of conservation movements than the nostalgia of an ex-trapper like myself.

My early outdoor life instilled in me an appreciation for the integrity of Nature. This feeling may be expressed otherwise as a love of Life—not Life in any narrow man-centered sense but Life in the sense of associations of plants and animals and physical environments that were age-tested long before man dominated the Earth or even was on it. As a participant in living processes, modern man has his place; but my view over the years is that Life collectively is a greater thing than mankind collectively. I do not believe that man, with his most exceptional capabilities for dominance as a living form, should dominate ruthlessly and irresponsibly the other living forms that also belong on Earth.

In questions of what living forms belong (and where and when and how much), I know that I am still influenced in my late fifties by some of the wilderness ideals of my youth—though I am willing to make some concessions forced upon me by realities. We patently cannot have wilderness everywhere and have the civilization we know today. Neither do I think, as responsible beings, we should consider ourselves entitled to obliterate wilderness everywhere. Recognizing that there have to be compromises, I should say that a civilized attitude would be to try to preserve a good deal of Nature in as natural condition as we can, if only for the sake of our own mental health. From our own selfish standpoints, the "good life" needs more than man and the man-made. To at least some civilized people, opportunities to enjoy and to reflect in the natural out-of-doors are as important as material comforts.

Of Man and Maturity

AN, LIKE THE WOLF, IS AN ANIMAL DOING WHAT
he does with what he has. Man's natural endowments differ from those of the wolf in degree; both
man and wolf are highly gifted as living things go.
Among the nonhuman animals, the dog family
may be rated as having exceptional intelligence,
and in this family the wolf has one of the superior brains. Moreover, the behavior of the wolf does not differ so fundamentally
from that of man at man's less advanced social levels. But the
wolf brain would appear to have relatively little left in unreal-
ized potentialities, and we may suspect that it never will be
much better than it is now.

I keep thinking of how really adept wolves can become in
staying alive and making a living despite human enmity. One
does not need to think only of the great "renegade" wolves such
as old Three Toes of Harding County, South Dakota, which
made man so conscious of their presence by the scale of their
depredations upon his livestock. The renegades included extremely wary individual wolves, but in my opinion the wolves
that live with minimal conspicuousness from man may represent still more advanced adaptation.

The most notable cases of adaptation with which I have had
close-at-hand experience were furnished by coyotes rather than
by the larger wolves, so my own illustrations shall be from coyotes.

Shortly after becoming an Iowa resident in the early thirties, I studied the prey remains outside of a coyote den in the
northwestern part of the state and wondered if this family could
keep out of trouble, living as it did in the roughest pasture and
marshland and subsisting only on wild prey and carrion. The
adults were obviously behaving with great respect toward inimical man, and except for my scientific colleagues and me, I

Atlantic Naturalist 23(4):195–203 (1968).

doubt if anyone suspected that there were coyotes in that part of the country at all—not until late summer when some members of the coyote family made their big mistake. My guess is that the young ones were those that advertised themselves by howling in response to train whistles.

Years later in central Iowa I discovered a coyote wintering within a few miles of the Iowa State University campus. For a time I followed its food habits, hoping that no one else would notice those tracks and other sign in the ravine where a farmer had left a dead hog. The home range of the coyote, however, happened to coincide with that of a highly skillful hunter whose hobby was hunting foxes by stalking and trailing, and the hunter saw all that he needed to see while the snow lasted.

Another central Iowa animal about which I had a chance to learn something was probably a dog-coyote hybrid with predominantly coyote features that a game warden brought in for identification. This creature had been seen off and on for a couple of years in the rough land of the Des Moines River valley near Boone. I do not know that it ever did any harm, but as soon as people knew it was there, they tried to shoot it. It outran, outsneaked, outhid, and eluded everybody and everything until the day that a high-powered expanding bullet reached far out and caught it. When I skinned it for a specimen, I found numerous shotgun pellets imbedded in the hide and a perfectly trained-down canine body—massive running muscles and practically no visible fat anywhere. The stomach contained some muddy bones and bristles from a carrion pig carcass.

Northern Minnesota wolves have been adjusting to man during the last two decades by becoming increasingly wary of the aircraft to which they had once been so vulnerable. They were observed to avoid the ice of lakes as aircraft approached in the winter of 1948–1949, after large numbers had been shot from the air during the previous two winters. And I have heard of Minnesota wolves detecting the approach of a plane before it even came into human view, to run off to shore for the concealment of the woods until the plane had passed—then back on the ice to continue on their way. It has taken some painful learning, for many wolves had to be killed far out on the ice before enough survived to discover what this was all about and gradually pass on the lesson of their experience to their fellows.

In contrast with the Iowa coyotes and the Lake States timber wolves, which as a result of human persecution may be using their brains close to the limit of their capabilities, I think that man collectively might be doing better than he does with the brain that he has.

I have acquired great admiration for the quality of headwork often displayed by members of the general public—the humor, the astuteness, the clever improvisations of people very nearly everywhere. If manifestations of genius are not frequently to be perceived at almost any time throughout most strata of human society, there are certainly manifestations of a high grade of intelligence as we define it. This may all be said without implying commensurate admiration for the quality of thinking man too often does with his naturally excellent brain.

In so stating I do not think that I am claiming perception and maturity that I myself do not have, for only within what happen to be my fields of competence do I feel especially qualified to examine the thinking of others. It is with respect to the overall fields of population ecology and dynamics, the so-called balance of nature, predators and predation, natural resources and outdoor values that I feel I have the most to offer in the way of constructive opinion.

The farther I go outside of these areas of my own personal competence or experience the more I can expect to do so at my own risk. Nevertheless, one should be entitled to ask questions. One question that recurs to me is: How much may public reactions to what is wild be symptomatic of immaturity?

Within the content implied by the title "Of Wilderness and Wolves," many greater or smaller topics could be singled out to illustrate immaturities in human thinking. I shall simply express my misgivings concerning man's continued wastage of the natural values of which we have little left to waste, his continued misappraisals of biological relationships that should no longer be subject to so much misappraisal, his continued imputation of moral evil where moral evil does not exist, and his continued punishment of wild animals for being what they are, for being wild and for living in the only ways that they could be expected to live.

Let us consider some of the exaggerations in mass attitudes toward wild creatures, especially toward predators and other wild species that may do damage under conditions favoring damage. "Control" of this or that wild species, intended in behalf of someone or something, has been notorious for the extremes to which it may lead. Down through the list of nearly everything that eats or digs or roosts or is suspected of doing something or of being something we have man's proscriptions, often without any semblance of balanced judgment.

I do not and never did maintain that we can always ignore economics in our philosophies concerning predators and predation. I am willing to reiterate as many times as need be that depredations of large wolves cannot be tolerated in a part of the country where they can do so much damage as, say, in South Dakota. There may be economic aspects to predation even by the much less formidable coyotes that man may be entitled to do something about; though in protecting his interests, I do not think he is entitled to overdo his campaigning.

It does not have to be that man always overdoes, and very practical people can set some good examples. In addition to the realism I have admired on the part of ranchers who felt they could have some coyotes around without having coyote damage if they took proper care of their livestock, I recall a fairly recent conversation with one of the neighbors near the old home farm in South Dakota, a man who lived at the edge of a hilly tract south of Lake Tetonkaha. He told me about a coyote den he could watch from his own yard. He, too, felt confident in being able to take care of his stock without killing the coyotes, and he watched the coyote pups playing unmolested as long as they occupied the den site. He made a point of telling me all about it with a certain exultation. What if the coyotes did kill some pheasants along with the jackrabbits and ground squirrels? There was plenty of game and plenty to spare, and it was not every day or every year that anyone could watch a family of coyotes growing up.

But, again, it seems that man's tendencies toward anything to be called reasonability or broad-mindedness or just governing his actions by facts can be less than they should be. The human capability for hatred without good reason is one of the things that may trouble me the most when I worry about whether man is mature enough for his position of dominance over the Earth.

I recall, as a graduate student, one of my earlier conversations with Aldo Leopold: he advised me to discount a certain viewpoint in a controversy on the grounds that the holder of the viewpoint was known as a hater and that haters seldom got matters wholly straight. In most cases it is not the actual perse-

113

cution of wild animals by this or that faction that troubles me so much as it is the intensity of the hatred so often underlying such persecution—and the narrowness, wilfulness, ignorance, and poor thinking that the hatred and persecution so much reflect. What makes sense in human motivation is one thing, but it is quite another thing when a psychological attitude can be paraphrased as: *It makes no difference what you say or do because we are going right ahead and do what we intend to do anyway.*

It may be a private matter of someone resisting all reason for the sake of his prejudices. It may be a legislature passing a worse-than-useless bounty law. Whether demagoguery is triumphant or merely unreason on an individual scale, we may still ponder the socially frightening aspects that it has.

Apart from our attitudes toward wild animals, may we not ask if this is the kind of thinking that motivates and directs us in great economic and political trials and in the safeguarding of what we regard as the precious gains made by our civilization? I do not know but am afraid that it is. There can be no doubt that in exaggerated forms our psychological immaturities are reflected by many inclinations to use power irresponsibly, to "throw weight around," to commit the outrages by which man can demean himself in any part of the world. At other extremes, we may only be naive.

What do we think of as civilization? More and more people and taller skyscrapers? Faster transportation? Universal gadgetry? Material comforts and leisure and entertainment? Fads and dogmas? Industrialization and the manners of holiday traffic, littering roadsides and scenic areas with trash? Or should it be progress toward understanding and reason?

Should not civilization mean better perspective, with neither arrogance nor self-abasement? Should it not mean evolution toward impartial regard for truth, toward what we know as good taste and decency and thoughtfulness, toward the maturity that man now needs as he probably never has needed it before?

It might be wholesome, if nothing more, for man to reflect critically upon his own relation to the modern world and upon his relations with the so-called lower animals, including some he professes to despise. He might do well not to switch unthinkingly from one opposing viewpoint to another, but rather to try to winnow what makes sense from what does not. It is just possible that if man showed a more truly enlightened and objective attitude toward other kinds of life, he might learn to show more toward his own.

By all means we should strive toward realism—toward realism in actuality, not toward the travesties of realism that may have labels of realism placed upon them.

Realism calls for a scale of proportions. The "either-or," "good or bad," "all or nothing" oversimplifications in our reasoning may offer us easy thought patterns and catchy slogans; they also can lead to appalling fallacies and to pogroms and wars along with lesser excesses.

Because the early settlers regarded wilderness as an enemy to conquer or something to exploit and because we cannot have wilderness everywhere and still maintain agriculture and industry, it should not follow that we cannot have wilderness anywhere.

Wilderness values are priceless to some people, even if more or less indefinable. They have meant a great deal in my own life, and in my earlier years, possibly as much as anything else. I need not be told that my love of wilderness is not uniformly shared by the public, for such an attitude would not be expected; but as wildernesses are increasingly encroached upon, more people show interest in preserving wilderness values.

Wilderness and what it stands for could mean still more in terms of human tranquillity and reflection in an era of artificiality and unrest. There is much that could be written about the needs for mental health and solid, constructive interests during times when the problems of nuclear threats and power politics, increasing uncertainty and increasing leisure, cults and juvenile gangs, and the whole array of man's social afflictions come as near to dominating our society as they do today. One need not be grasping for Utopias to see the psychological illness manifested by our young delinquents. I have seen dull-faced adolescents in Europe as well as at home in the United States, spitting on sidewalks, bored with everything, going around looking for excitement, just any kind of diversion, and maybe making some. Delinquency is nothing new in human history, and my home neighborhood had its equivalent of delinquents during my youth—reflecting then the same cynical escapism of the modern delinquents, the parasitic philosophies, and the strong appeal of their own kinds of conformities.

I am thankful again that I liked to hunt and fish and trap and camp and do target shooting and go for long walks in the natural out-of-doors, that I had some companions who liked to do the same things (if not always to the extent that I did), and that some of the natural out-of-doors existed close by. I am thankful that I liked to read, that I had access to what was worth reading, and that I could achieve at least a passable balance between indoor and outdoor pursuits. I am thankful for interests that could compete—as long as any competition could be said to have existed in my own case—with the diversions that only divert.

Without advancing any panaceas, I submit that what remains of our natural out-of-doors, of our wilderness and what belongs in it, is worth keeping. I shall not say that keeping it will be cheap or easy or without opposition or without the confusion of differing objectives.

There are always the questions of what retention of any natural wildness in a mechanized and crowded human society may cost, whether any possible gains in this respect would be worth the price, economically or otherwise.

Here, too, some of the most twisted reasoning may be advanced, perhaps honestly, perhaps with a sly profit motive concealed somewhere in the wording. I think especially of the agitation against nature preserves in or near great metropolitan areas on the grounds that their lonely trails and concealing vegetation may provide a setting for crime and that they are unsafe for people to visit—that they would serve society better if they were to be cleared and leveled and used for parking lots or housing developments. Secluded wild places may in truth be places for robbery, rape, and sadistic murders as criminals spill over into them from the slum districts. But what irony there is in the argument that because of the evils of the slums, we must get rid of something that offers to at least some people who need it at least a partial relief from those evils.

We may be informed that a single human life is so precious as to outweigh any possible advantage of a wild area. I do not deny that human life can be precious, but the arguments leading to such open-and-shut conclusions can be farcical. The three central Iowa marshes that I know best have each been the site of at least one accidental human death during the years I have known them. National parks have their fatalities of both visitors and park personnel. What recreational waters may not over the years have tragedies or chances for tragedies? Yet, in terms of danger to human life, what really compares with our highways? What highways have ever been left unbuilt merely because of the possibility—the certainty—that people will in time be killed upon them?

The body of one of my family's best friends lies under avalanche debris in a great mountain wilderness in Asia. He was in his midtwenties, at the end of his graduate training, a young man of the finest character and promise. His death meant a great personal sorrow to me. A wilderness killed him, and had it not been for his love of wilderness, he would not have been there to be killed. The mountaineering tragedy that took his life is no disproof of the pricelessness of mountains and wildernesses and the values they stand for to modern man. If anyone were to ask me if I would feel the same way if I had been the one to lose a son, I am sure I would say that I would feel the same.

This is nothing that I like to contemplate, for I want no sorrow for anyone to result from wholesome outdoor interests; but it points up a homely fact that there have to be lines drawn somewhere in the consideration of different kinds and degrees of values. Even something as precious as human life has to be considered in reference to something else, to what may be meaningful among other values. There are still questions as to what values make life worth having.

There are still questions as to what we as a public are willing to risk and pay in terms of money, effort, and patience for outdoor values. We are willing to expend—according to the more liberal estimates—into the billions of dollars annually as well as vast effort to go on vacations into wild and scenic country. Our investment in equipment for hunting, fishing, camping, boating, skiing, and traveling, in accommodations and special licenses and guiding fees and transportation charges, may add up to impressive totals even for single individuals or families. No doubt about it—we can and will pay for the enjoyment of the out-of-doors when we are of a mind to. And we can work hard at extracting enjoyment from what we do in the out-of-doors.

What are we willing to invest in money, time, ingenuity, and undramatic purposeful endeavor to safeguard the essential features of what we are willing to spend so freely to find and enjoy in the out-of-doors? Or are we willing to let our outdoor values be continually watered down or whittled down or lost by default, while we travel farther and farther in search of them and hope that somewhere, someplace, there will always be something remaining of them that is worth having, seeing, or thinking about? Or do we just give up, talk about what we had or did when we were young or how we should have been born in the pioneering days or settle for having our out-of-doors brought inside for us via TV?

As concerns the preservation of wilderness or the essential features thereof, we can rather count on its costing money and having its troublesome aspects. Whether the necessary expenditures and efforts in behalf of wild land or wild creatures must be channeled into purchases, maintenance, indemnities for damage, educational campaigns, or something else, it all must cost. Outdoor values are unlikely to take care of themselves, with man's swarming increase and delusions as to what he calls "conquest of Nature."

When thinking of public indemnities as a part of the price for protection of outdoor values, I think of more than possible damage to livestock from any kind of predation. Hoofed game may also have expensive habits in relation to human property that gets in its way—all one needs to do is to inquire about wapiti herds where these are abundant in the American West. Waterfowl depredations on farm crops in concentration areas may be sufficient to arouse local agitation for exterminating our already overhunted and drained-out ducks and geese; as a general public we have sufficient interest in the ducks and geese as prized game to resist any such nonsensical extremes, but we still must be as fair as we can be toward other people who may have genuine grievances against the ducks and geese.

Besides the wapiti and the ducks and geese, moose and sandhill cranes and a considerable variety of other valuable and interesting nonpredacious species may all be among those we cannot permit to be slaughtered merely because of their sometimes very real damage to private property. When the damage by these species in which the public claims ownership cannot be prevented by feasible and bloodless means, one alternative may be for the public to pay compensation for the damages resulting.

In Sweden, hunters' organizations contribute funds for

compensating private people not only for damages done by favorite game species but also by certain predators, including those that the Swedes are trying to safeguard from extermination in their country.

I propose, in substance, that the American public regard its own rare species of all kinds—whether predatory or not but especially the rare large predators—as public charges. The public should assume responsibility to safeguard these species and to compensate for private damages that must inevitably result now and then from free-living animals. This responsibility should embrace the grizzly and Alaskan brown and polar bears, the wolverine, and cougar, the Canada lynx, and the large wolves, all to the extent that their needs require treatment as public charges.

Surely, again, this would cost. I do not feel capable of calculating how much, but if the cost be compared to the cost for a mile of newly paved highway or some tampering with a river or virtually any pork-barrel measure, I am sure we could afford to pay.

Managing wolves according to what I should regard as enlightened criteria would call for appraisals and reappraisals of local, regional, national, and international situations. Balanced against each other should be the wolf's high reproductive potential, the wolf's potentialities for damage, the excessive persecution to which the wolf is subject, and the danger that at least certain forms may be totally lost.

Already, for North America, E. A. Goldman has listed five of twenty-three modern subspecies of true wolves, *Canis lupus*, as either extinct, probably extinct, or extremely rare, and four others as having greatly reduced ranges. These geographical casualties were all severe competitors for man's livestock. Irrespective of how much it may be reasoned that these wolves had to go, in every case where man has destroyed or doomed a subspecies, he has destroyed some evolution. It is or should be a solemn matter to obliterate a highly developed form of Life so finally. Civilized man should have sufficient regret in having done so to avoid repetitions through unnecessary heavy-handedness.

The wolves of some North American subspecies having greatly reduced geographic ranges may already be precariously reduced. But other wolves, including the eastern wolf or the one we usually call the timber wolf, may still be in no immediate danger of extinction.

The latter is probably true for most of the Canadian subspecies. Nevertheless, human pressure even upon wilderness forms can be intensive through the use of aircraft and poison over vast areas of the northern parts of the northern hemisphere. Both the Canadians and the Russians may campaign against wilderness wolves with an effectiveness that leads one to question how racially secure some truly wilderness wolves may be. Remoteness from centers of human populations may afford a wolf population a tremendous advantage in its relations with man, but, except when the wolves have the further advantage of a protective terrain, remoteness may not necessarily insure their safety. Large predators in the Far North can be notably vulnerable to human persecution if man wants to lay it on, up there on the frozen landscape when food may be scarce and localized and the snow and ice fields and open tundra and tree-limit "bush" give little concealment from men in planes on days of good visibility.

Rational handling of the wolf problem may require campaigning against the wolves when and where they should be kept down, easing up on the campaigning or even protecting them when and where they need it, and trying at all times to keep them in the right balance as a resource of value as well as a pest. It is the sort of thing concerning which decisions and actions should be governed by the requirements of each particular situation, as of the particular time and place.

Apart from such generalizations that whatever is decided or done should be to the best interests of the wolves, the best interests of their prey, and the best interests of the wildernesses in which wolves and their prey belong, what I have in mind is nothing that fits together in convenient formulas. It is nothing that is covered too well by slogans or other substitutes for thinking. There is nothing cheap or easy about it at all.

Can it be said that many of the highest, best aims with respect to almost anything worth having are cheaply or easily attainable? How much in the way of solutions to any problems really stays put? The old sayings about eternal vigilance being the price we must pay for great values have very hard truths in them, as people have learned over and over. May we not just assume that extremely little about Life ever remains settled?

As one whose sympathies are with wilderness wolves, I would need something more than the prospect of a pelt, bounty payment, or sport to make me now want to shoot one. On the other hand, I am not opposed to their being hunted in moderation, even in our northern Lake States where I regard our timber wolf remnant as being of outstanding value. A hunting toll that is restricted to the annual surplus or its equivalent can be borne by well-situated wolves as well as by other well-situated animals.

Moreover, I think that it would be a good thing if the public would come to regard wolves as game animals in the places where wolves belong—fair game themselves, within limits, and not just thought of or spoken of in outmoded cliches as enemies of game. That would not need to be contrary to good wildlife management, and it might substitute for some of the hysteria that wolves currently elicit.

As one who has killed for a livelihood, which I did in my trapping years, and as one who still likes to hunt, I confess that I do not care for the kind of sport hunting or "varmint shooting" that fails to utilize the animals killed. I do not, however, insist that mine is the only true faith in this respect. If sport hunting were done honestly, humanely, and with a proper regard for the amount of hunting pressure that the hunted species could stand, I certainly would have less objection to it than I feel toward much that I know goes on.

Why cannot a hunter who has, through his own skill, bagged a wolf in a fair hunt be satisfied with the feat, with the pelt or trophy or the demonstration of his stamina or woodsmanship, with the recreation he may have gotten from the hunting? Why can he not consider that he has enjoyed a privilege, without pouring out words about ridding the land of a killer? And if for any reason wolves or anything else be killed as a control measure, why cannot it be done without man, the killer, berating nonhuman creatures as being unfit to live?

To reiterate the thesis of this essay: man needs to do some growing up. This need is manifested among other ways by the emotional unreason he tends to show toward the behavior of wild creatures. The immoderations and inconsistencies in his attitude toward wolves or other predatory or competing species are particularly revealing of lack of maturity.

The bounds of knowledge should not be considered merely as something set by professional groups. Trained minds are not always free from biases, and training is only as good as teachers and the receptivity of students make it. Knowledge must still be judged on the basis of whether a given person has the information necessary to justify conclusions, whether he has the ability and intention to follow evidence where it leads, and whether he can distinguish between what he knows and what he does not know.

My own lack of confidence in the results of public thought on animal populations and related subjects does not mean that I would discourage public thought about such things. Very definitely, what I am trying to do is to encourage more and better thinking—not necessarily thinking that agrees with mine in all or even most respects, but thinking that takes realities into account. So far as I am concerned, anyone is entitled to a respectful hearing to the extent that he deserves it, but he will have to do better than to repeat old misconceptions and to attempt to speak authoritatively on topics outside of his fields of competence.

Man does desperately need to grow up. His claims to conquests of Nature are farcical in the perspective of the problems converging upon him. Modern refinements and gadgets notwithstanding, he is still much a savage who wants to impose his domination where he wishes and make it stick.

He certainly has gained physical power. As a species he now can obliterate nearly anything he can reach. He can build or destroy as no other inhabitants of this Earth have done before. Within wide limits he has, figuratively, attained a good share of the stature of the Olympian gods he thought up centuries ago. What is wrong is that his is still too much the psychology of the Olympian gods whom he originally invested with pettiness and jealousies, primitive motivations, and whimsical concepts of justice.

And there is man figuratively sitting on Olympus with his hands full of thunderbolts, draining marshes, damming rivers, flying supersonic planes, and inflicting his vengeance upon wolves for being wolves. There is man, whose social and ecological impacts have become increasingly out of proportion to his responsibility. There he is, far from being mature enough to toss thunderbolts in every direction; needing more than anything else to learn to live with the intelligence, dignity, restraint, and goodness he somewhere has in him.

Of A Wolf Named Dagwood

LGONQUIN PROVINCIAL PARK IS AN IRREGU-
larly blocked-off area that averages out at about
fifty by sixty miles. It lies only about a hundred
and twenty-five miles northeast of Toronto and
less than a hundred west of Ottawa, but it is
northern wilderness in the midst of wilderness. At
one time the park was managed more than it is now to attract
the conventional tourist visitors. Now, the emphasis is upon the
values of solitude and wild beauty. Canoe routes are accessible
by road from only a few places, and camp and picnic grounds,
public docks, concessions, and park-maintained buildings are
localized along a paved highway that cuts through little more
than a corner of the park.

Long ago the lumbermen took the big pines; and old tote
roads and other reminders of human activity are still visible
even in some of the remote parts of the park. The forester still
works in places today, and fire lookout towers are situated
about ten miles apart. But the park does include and is surrounded by great expanses of wilderness—wilderness properly
designated as such even though it cannot rate as primeval
wilderness. It has the creatures native to northern
wildernesses, including wolves and wolf prey.

The purpose of the Ontario government's work on wolves in
Algonquin Park and elsewhere is to acquire a sound factual
basis for wolf management. Such management, when the factual basis exists, may call either for control of wolves or for
protection of wolves, or measures in between, depending upon
what the local and provincial situations may be.

In early December 1960 I had an opportunity to spend a few
days with Douglas Pimlott on the Ontario government's wolf-
study area at Algonquin Park.

The Pimlott family had raised a litter of five wolves during
the summer preceding my visit, living together with them,
children and all, on an island. The wolves had had the free run

123

of the island, except for property that had to be fenced in to protect it from puppy teeth—the tent ropes and clothing and instrument cases that could be damaged because of the chewing impulses of puppyhood.

After transfer from the island to a big cage, one young wolf had found an electric extension cord left behind by a photographer, had cut it up into short sections, eaten some of it, and died.

The four survivors included wolves differing greatly in temperament. Two, Dagwood and Blondie, were happy extroverts, friendly toward everyone; and Blondie had been taken away from the station to learn how much the equivalent of a domestic dog might be made of her. Dagwood remained at the station with two other litter members, both females: One, called Lup (from *lupus*), was as friendly and happy as Dagwood but not such a positive character, and the other, called Kit, was very sensitive and shy of strangers.

Pimlott took me into the cage with him on his return after an absence of several days. He advised me to keep an arm up to my face, but I did not fully realize what kind of welcome I, as a stranger, would get from even the tamer wolves and I did not have my arms up high enough. The first thing I knew, I had been nipped in the face by both Dagwood and Lup, as they had leapt over my upraised arm. Then I got my arm up higher. After some more leaping, the two wolves quieted down and became merely a couple of dogs that mouthed my mittened hands and wriggled and rubbed their heads against me as I patted them.

Feeling the gentleness of those sharp teeth on my face (they did not come anywhere near breaking skin) and the tooth points that came through two thicknesses of heavy knitted mittens only to touch my hands, I remembered Lois Crisler's reference to gentle grooming by the teeth of her wolves.

Kit, the third wolf, never stopped watching me even while greeting Pimlott, whom she trusted. Hoping to see her at ease, I would withdraw from the vicinity of the cages and sneak back to peek around tree trunks or thickets or the edges of buildings. No matter what I tried, any time that I could see her, she was looking at me. Once Pimlott had been forced to seize her, and the experience had been so upsetting to her that it had taken weeks of patient handling to bring back her confidence in him. Her social attachments were toward Dagwood and Lup and the family's Labrador retriever and toward the Pimlott children; and when she was left alone in the cage, she howled and howled, howling the short "lonesome" howl, with a drop at the end.

In late afternoon of my first day at the research station, I had a chance to romp with Dagwood alone, about the cages and down along a road and a lakeshore. He had gotten past his earlier cavorting mood and now ran and sniffed and ate snow in a matter-of-fact way, occasionally returning to the vicinity of the cages to greet everybody and be friends. As he came up to me to rub against my parka, I would give his big head a shake and call him a mutt. When it was time for Dagwood to be put back into the cage, Pimlott just reached down, gathered up an armful of docile, satisfied wolf and carried the limp animal over to the cage door. Not any trouble, not the least, all between the best of friends; and it was a happy Dagwood that we left in the cage.

Dagwood at seven months weighed about sixty pounds on a frame for about eighty to a hundred. His feet, spread out, left tracks nearly as large as my hand, spread out.

Two times in two days we took Dagwood and Lup for long walks along a trail leading through the bush. They ate snow, circled and explored, engaged in hiding and chasing games. Lois Crisler wrote that wolves did not run, they flowed; and Dagwood and Lup flowed over the trails, over and under windfalls, and through the balsams and deciduous brush. They were as close to the embodiment of grace as anything animate I ever saw, and so joyous, so much at ease, and so friendly. There was no master-servant relationship between Pimlott and the wolves; they stayed with us or returned to us in response to howling because of their own will, as friends; and, when Pimlott picked each up to put it back in the cage at the end of the outing, each went trustingly limp.

On the second day that we took Dagwood and Lup for a long walk we were out of contact with them for a couple of hours. We thought that Dagwood and Lup might have met and joined a wild one off in the bush. We walked while Pimlott howled. Pimlott and I separated so as to cover more ground, and, off by myself, I knew from lonesome Kit's continued howling back in the cage that it was as yet of no use for me to come in. Finally, the strays were howled in at the far end of the trail that we had first made, and they came back without any further nonsense. Everything was all right as each armful of wolf was gathered up and dropped in through the cage door.

Pimlott was less worried about Dagwood in particular joining wild wolves than about his getting lost before knowing enough about hunting and other facts of a normal wolf's life to take care of himself. Dagwood was much more than an expendable experimental animal. Pimlott wished to do right by this splendid creature; he wished to insure for Dagwood an optimum freedom that a wolf should have, together with protection from people if it had free run of the park.

Dagwood did wander down to the highway on one occasion, and human friends who knew him found him there wholly by chance. The danger was not only that some wolf hater might deliberately run him down with an automobile but also that some stranger on foot might be frightened at the sight of a big wolf running toward him the way Dagwood runs—Dagwood, the hearty extrovert who trusts and likes everybody.

Nothing about this had easy answers, and it was not the first time that people who have been friends with wolves have had like problems.

I last saw Dagwood looking at me from the big cage of the tame wolves shortly after daybreak on a Sunday morning. He would have romped, I am sure, but Pimlott and I had other things on our minds. We were trying to start the third of three motor vehicles that would not start at thirty-nine below zero, and I had a plane reservation for three o'clock that afternoon at the Toronto airport.

Afterward, I could think about Dagwood some more, about how much he might be a living answer to old questions as to where domestic dogs originally came from, or at the least to questions concerning the degree of tamability a wolf could have. Whatever a wolf might need in the way of psychological undercurrents to be friendly toward man, Dagwood seemed to have them. He had been shown on TV. He had unselfconsciously howled on a lecture platform before a large audience in response to an invitation to howl. Life among people as he knew it had been good; and so far as I could see, he accepted most things as they were.

There was not much of the obedient servant to be seen in Dagwood, little if anything more than what the tame wolves of prehistory may have shown the campfire men. He was no wolf to object to minor infringements of his liberties, as when picked up and deposited inside the cage door. That was a normal part of his life, with nothing disquieting about it, all consistent with his own experience and nature as an amiable, tolerant, and happy wolf. His restraint in using sharp teeth on friends was consistent with his nature as a wolf and did not represent any trained-dog type of responsibility.

Dagwood was still a wolf, certainly far from being an immediate predecessor of a lapdog or herdsman's dog or any other artificially bred-up form of domestic dog. He was the product of evolutionary refinement of a different sort. He was built for agility, endurance, and power, to rip through animal tissue in preying upon large game—although as a seven-months pup he had never killed his own food—and to fast or gorge if that was what was required of him as a wolf. His eating manners were those long sanctioned by his line of descent: a few snaps, a few gulps, and he had fed, "wolfing" food even when alone and unhurried. To this limited extent, man's traditional concept of wolfishness was not inconsistent with the reality of the wolf, Dagwood.

Dagwood, in his basic wolfishness, remained in my estimation essentially unspoiled despite his close association with man. He was himself, in his sinuous body and expressive face, his alert intelligence, and in the curiosity, mischievousness, and friendliness that he so openly showed. Dagwood's behavior, along with that of the tame wolves of the centuries, might be construed as saying, "Take us as we are and we can be friends, but do not expect of us what we are not and have not."

I do not claim to be a dog man—that is, any owner or trainer of dogs. Possibly I have not really liked more than a dozen or so individual dogs in my whole life; and fewer still are those I would have wanted to own.

I would not want Dagwood, either, as an animal to be owned, even if I had the time and means for taking care of him; for I do not think that ownership in the usual sense would be compatible with what is best and most interesting about him. I enjoyed him because he was his own wolf, notwithstanding his faculty for putting a strange human at ease.

IV

OF CONSERVATION

THE FOLLOWING TWO ESSAYS, "A QUESTION of Values," and "The Pricelessness of Untampered Nature," were both published in the Journal of Wildlife Management—*the first in summer of 1947 and the second, posthumously, in spring of 1963.*

In "A Question of Values" Paul wrote as a hunter: "To me, with gun in hand or without, the appeal of the out-of-doors seems chiefly conditioned by the relative diversity and completeness of its native fauna and flora and the naturalness of its topography." For him, hunter though he was, "sport purchased at disproportionate cost to [such] outdoor values was not worth having."

Incidentally, "A Question of Values" was more widely reprinted, both in the United States and abroad, than any article he ever wrote.

"The Pricelessness of Untampered Nature" was Paul's last essay. Here, speaking as a practical conservationist, he suggests ways in which natural areas close to home may be kept natural without either much expense or effort.

COLLEAGUES AND FRIENDS SOMETIMES WENT
WITH PAUL ON FIELD TRIPS.
Photo, Marion Ferguson

A Question of Values

OVER AND OVER AGAIN, PRACTITIONERS IN THE professional field of wildlife management are asked and ask themselves exactly what they work for. To increase game, to make hunting easier, to control pests, to hold their jobs, or what? Among other things I suppose I may be classed as a wildlife manager, having made a living for nearly twenty years by doing research on game birds and fur bearers and having published findings that presumably apply to what is known as management of those species. Like my co-workers in the field, I have been asked and have asked myself basic questions.

I am pleased when good use is made of my research by conservation commissions and other practical agencies. Yet, if I felt that I merely worked for a salary and to provide more game for hunters to shoot or more fur for trappers to catch, I probably would not want to remain in the profession. If I did not feel that I might be working for something more important than my own or any other person's selfish advantage, a drudgery and strain that I have come to accept as an unavoidable accompaniment of my lifework would be burdensome, indeed.

I am in no position to undertake here a comprehensive discussion of human motivations in the field of wildlife management or out of it. I had even better leave out of consideration some very strong scientific and sociological motivations and restrict this essay in scope to a few aspects suggesting denominators common to wildlife managers and, let us say, the hunters and trappers.

From early youth to midtwenties, or up to the beginning of my graduate training, I earned my living largely by fur trapping. This was my recognized vocation, and it usually paid off in cash as well as any other I could have had at the time. But some of the trapping seasons I enjoy recalling were among the

Journal of Wildlife Management 11(3): 267–72 (1947).

less profitable economically. My two most ambitious expeditions (which in the end perhaps yielded me as much enduring satisfaction as anything I ever did as a young man) were business failures. Moreover, the drawbacks of a trapper's life as I lived it ruled out money as a full explanation for the attraction trapping may hold for civilized man. Nor am I convinced that prospects for adventure are any more of an explanation. Part of the answer lies in the intangibles, in chickadees fluffing themselves into feathery balls and tree trunks popping in the northwoods cold, in grouse budding in aspen thickets at dusk, in sun dogs hanging over the western plains, in clean air and freedom, and in the sweet loneliness expressed by passages in Sibelius's "Finlandia."

I was also a hunter during my trapping years. I won't lay claim to having been the idealized sportsman of whom I read in outdoor magazines. I wasn't, and I shot more for meat than for sport, but at any rate I know the hunter's side of hunting.

In the eastern South Dakota of my upbringing were chain after chain of glacial lakes, marshes, and potholes, with ducks in variety and numbers possibly not found anywhere on Earth since the decade following the First World War. Like other hunters, I have my memories of the folding of birds singled out of flocks whipping over the rushes, of the impacts of falling bodies on the water, of drifting feathers and the smell of powder smoke.

For all of that, I must confess that my hunting memories are not as a rule memories of shooting or of bag limits.

One October afternoon I sat on a ridge between two of the Tetonkaha Lakes adjoining our family's home farm. The day was warm and still, and I saw only scattered, high-flying ducks until sundown. Then a redhead flight started from the west. The birds were flying out of shotgun range, so I just continued to sit. Flock following flock, the sound of their passage roared over land and water like the sound of an express train crossing a trestle. I doubt not that I was disappointed to go home without any of those ducks, but the vision that stays with me is one of the color and power of redheads pouring down onto the lake.

Another occasion on which there was more shooting comes to mind. The numbers of waterfowl I saw on a raw, windy day at Lake Albert in 1927 hardly compared with those to be seen when my grandparents lived in their sod shanty in the Tetonkaha hills, nor with the numbers existing in my childhood

132

when men would come home with all of the ducks they could carry and guns would flash on the marshes late into the evening. Nevertheless, on this day, there were in view on the horizon mallards in flocks of hundreds and thousands, and these were interspersed by an unending succession of smaller flocks and stragglers. The ducks that furnished our shooting were mainly lesser scaups.

The scaups were high, wide, and fast; they were low, close, and fast; they came tumbling and zigzagging down from the heights on slanted wings to skim over the water; they swept by in compact bunches or in open arcs or in irregular formation. The shooting was extremely "sporty," though attended by exasperating losses of dead and crippled birds because of the roughness of the water. Now, I find that day most pleasing in retrospect if I simply think of ducks in the air.

Nor do all of my hunting memories relate to panoramic spectacles. I recall a day spent along the Sioux River, west of Brookings, South Dakota. I don't know what my bag was but it wasn't large—a mallard brought down by a lucky snapshot through an opening in the treetops, a green-winged teal, and maybe a couple of cottontail rabbits. I don't remember what else if anything I may have shot, and I don't care to. What I do remember was the contrast of the white wedge on the dark head of a hooded merganser swimming in a patch of open water. I stood watching it from the underbrush until it saw me and took wing, to disappear around the bend and to leave to me the empty setting of water and wet snow.

Memories arise that are still more gunless, of the slow wing beats and sailing of white pelicans; of curlews, avocets, and hosts of smaller shorebirds; of muskrats floating on the marshes at sunset, their tails crooked in the air. There are memories of spawning pickerel in the shallows and herons standing along the lakeshores and ground squirrels in the pastures. There are memories of ordinary and trivial things.

Ordinary or trivial as may be the substance of these memories, they are my prize trophies from the out-of-doors. How much the values underlying them may be identified with James Norman Hall's "spirit of place" I am not sure, but unquestionably they are of it. One spring day long after my trapping years, I walked the banks of a creek familiar to my youth and was depressed because of having seen no mink tracks on mud bars where I knew there should have been some. Those mink tracks in my mind were integral to the "spirit of place" of that creek, and no amount of the crowing of introduced pheasants could compensate for their lack.

Nostalgia doubtless enters into the equation, but again I can not say how much. The pronghorn antelope, the anhinga, the limpkin, the sage grouse, and the woodland caribou were not creatures of my early background; and I have never seen a musk-ox, polar bear, black-footed ferret, or ptarmigan living in the wild. Even so, I don't believe that I fail to appreciate how unmistakably they may belong in their respective habitats. One may easily go on and list at random almost any number of organisms, plants, and animals, similarly belonging in their own biotic communities: flying squirrels in aspen stubs, white-footed mice climbing in the underbrush, cypress draped with long moss, and lions under sandstone bluffs, fungi and crawling life under dead leaves.

Whether or not I ever again do any fur trapping, I am still a hunter and dream of spending my declining days amid an abundance of game sufficient for me to shoot some of it without feeling ashamed of myself. As a hunter I am interested in management programs having promise for increasing the game I like to hunt. That can be acknowledged without implying that my enthusiasm for a given program is proportional to the success with which it may increase the game, irrespective of damage to other outdoor values resulting from the means employed.

To me, with gun in hand or without, the appeal of the out-of-doors seems chiefly conditioned by the relative diversity and completeness of its native fauna and flora and the naturalness of its topography.

Although we may not anticipate a general return of bison herds to the central plains of North America as long as we retain our present social and economic system, the perpetuation of much of our natural out-of-doors is not incompatible with modernity. The growing literature on integration of ends for sound and permanent land use contradicts the thesis that "progress" must inevitably be accompanied by what we have been pleased to call the "conquest of Nature," with its top-heavy artificialities and its wastefulness.

Many of the problems of conservation and management are vexatious and appallingly involved. It is not hard to understand why conservation or management practice (or policy) has not been free from confusion and cross-purposes or how it may be guided less by long-time than by immediate objectives. In common with other human endeavors, conservation or management probably always will be attended by its share of futility and shortsightedness. Regrettable though this may be, worse still is the outright destruction of the values needing most to be preserved—especially in management programs sponsored by agencies subject to public pressure or catering to circumscribed groups.

It is fitting to strive for "businesslike" efficiency in wildlife management and to take aggressive action to stay or reverse the forces that impoverish the continent. Management, in the sense of judicious manipulation both of organisms and of their environment, should be legitimate and desirable as long as the price is not too great.

The chief mistakes in management practice that I have seen in my professional experience fall in two categories. The writings of Aldo Leopold and O. J. Murie have dealt with the first—the "cleaning up" and "doctoring" of places that should be left alone. The opening of roads, the cutting of grass, brush, and dead trees, the thinning of timber, the planting of exotic vegetation, the building of feeding stations, shelters, and bird houses, the breeding of wild animals in pens, are proper activities of man but they should not be carried on everywhere; and whenever man's ancient weakness for painting lilies becomes translated into artificializing in the name of wildlife management the remnants of natural out-of-doors that some regions have left, we need to take our collective bearings. What if a wilderness be comparatively unproductive in game yields or commercial assets if its own intrinsic values outweigh the ones it might conceivably gain through artificial changes?

Not many years ago I visited an island in a marsh, and my first impression was one of exceptional solitude and wild beauty, of a place where, despite the surrounding farm lands, a person wanting relief from human banalities might enjoy an illusion of remoteness. The illusion, however, could not withstand the reality of the series of game shelters that had been cut out of the island's trees.

In the second category of mistakes falls a vast amount of the "control" of native vertebrates advocated or conducted by this or that faction.

The traditional emphasis placed by sportsmen upon campaigning against the predatory or competitive species they designate as "vermin" is seldom based on adequate study. In too many instances it betrays the confusion introduced by mixed variables and cherished "fallacies of misplaced concreteness." Predation and competition being manifestations of life are, like life, phenomena of many complexities that do not always work out as it may be taken for granted they should. Suppression of predators or of competitors does not necessarily mean benefit to the game or more game to shoot; it is not a panacea and on the whole—though not entirely—shows less promise with investigation.

If, however, vermin control had many times over the effectiveness ascribed by its proponents, its use as an instrument of game or wildlife management would be no less in need of tempering with moderation and discrimination. Let it be understood that among the so-called vermin are some of our most beautiful and valuable of wild creatures. They comprise a resource demanding sane administration as much as any class of wildlife.

At its worst, vermin control may be carried on with an almost unbelievable pointlessness and intolerance. One may scarcely bring to mind a living thing larger than a tree frog that is not vermin to someone—and that includes game species in alleged behalf of which someone else may be shooting up the out-of-doors. I have seen hunters deliberately trying to shoot every shoveller—an easily killed duck and one greatly reduced a few years back—that came within gunshot range, to leave the carcasses where they fell, with remarks that the birds weren't fit to eat and ought to be cleaned out.

The coyote, the crow, and other adaptable and widely distributed predators are not the ones that are endangered by the anti-vermin crusades and the ceaseless killing as opportunities offer. It is the irresponsible harassment of species which "can't take it" that should cause us the most concern—the raptorial and fish-eating birds of restricted geographic range or of strikingly diminished numbers, the predatory fur bearers that are gravely enough depleted by overtrapping and shrinkage of habitats, the slow breeding, the unwary, the bizarre, the big and tempting targets. Luckless may be the rare or waning species that concentrates conspicuously in localities where it is vulnerable to raiding by man, notably if it be charged with "harmful" habits.

136

In my opinion it is highly dubious strategy to propagandize in favor of mass action for the "control" of native predators, to accelerate wholesale persecution by contest awards, bounties, and the sanction of influential organizations. The prejudices against wild flesh eaters are so entrenched in people's minds that encouragement may invite excesses and further squandering of what we may not have to spare. When even school children are urged to go out and kill an interminable variety of wild animals as vermin, we should not be surprised at the peculiar turns love of the out-of-doors may take.

Writing as a hunter, I would say that sport purchased at disproportionate cost to other outdoor values is not worth having. Wildlife management will be found very much wanting if it fails to safeguard any but popular game species and, incidentally, the song birds and unnoticed forms that are likely to thrive, anyway.

Hunter though I am, why should I have to be a hunter to gain caste, to be entitled to more than outdoor leftovers that may escape gun or pole trap? Why should I not dawdle on a hilltop in the hazy autumn sunshine if I would rather do that than go hunting, and if I choose not to hunt, why should it follow that I automatically relinquish to hunters all of my rights in game or in wild animals associated with game? To the extent that I as a citizen am mindful of the courtesies due others, I think I should be entitled to a certain freedom in my choice of outdoor pleasures, without carrying the insignia of gun any more than of rod or field glass or camera or hiking kit. If management itself is to be in analysis anything except exploitation, it must guard against the fundamental wrongness of giving me, upon payment of a piddling license fee, more shooting privileges than I deserve, at the same time shortchanging me as a citizen.

Herein lies a most serious obstacle to harmonious cooperation of outdoor groups in matters that should be to their mutual interest. The harvesting of a seasonal game crop through hunting isn't always the bitterest source of dissention between sportsman and "protectionist." Far more may be attributed to the blindness and selfishness of too many of the sportsmen and their leaders and their assurance that not only is the game theirs to shoot if they want to but also that theirs is the prerogative of doing about whatever they may wish with wildlife in general.

Flatly, I would say that it is time for hunters to reappraise their position in terms other than what they can get by with. I regard hunting logically justifiable only insofar as it may be done without real detriment to both game and nongame species, which means in short that the hunting toll (bagged and lost) of a given species be pretty well confined to biological surpluses. If I were to continue to hunt a severely declining species—though the primary cause of the decline be something besides shooting—I would consider myself justly entitled to fewer rights than the nonshooters. It is perfectly fair to expect me as a hunter to make concessions when that is the decent thing to do, as during emergency crises, the depressed phases of periodic cycles, years of overshooting, and so on.

Of course this too reflects in part my philosophy as a wildlife manager. It may or may not be that of others, but at least the profession could rightly accept something of the broader responsibilities implied by the leadership it exerts and the degree of custody it in effect holds over outdoor values that are not to be reckoned as material harvests. The issue is not one of management versus no management, but rather of what management should be and where it should be done; the criteria of accomplishment may be conformity to good taste as well as statistical impressiveness. Within reason, we and our editorialized but cheated posterity should be able to think of wildernesses extending beyond highways, of barren grounds and ice fields and deserts and unlogged forests and untampered lakes and streams. We should know of marshes with sandhill cranes and the more retiring of water birds, of rivers where otters live, of mountains where martens, fishers, wolverines, cougars, wolves, grizzly bears, and native sheep and goats exist in some security. Close to home, we should be able to find natural retreats in appropriate places, to see an eagle, osprey, loon, or one of the larger falcons on occasion; still to watch, among the sights that belong, the redtailed hawk in the sky; still to hear, among the night sounds, the hooting of the horned owl in the woods.

The Pricelessness of Untampered Nature

ANY YEARS AGO A GREAT UNIVERSITY decided—through its appropriate committees—to do something constructive about its arboretum. The interest in the arboretum was there, an articulate interest, and an interest sufficient to make money available. The land was the property of the university. It included the marshy edge of a lake, a natural bog, and a tract of possibly ten acres of nearly virgin forest in some sixty acres of oak-hickory woods.

The stated emphasis in managing the arboretum was to be placed upon protection and planting. Land was to be cleared to make room for plantings, and trees and shrubs and flowers were to be planted and planted in fulfillment of the foresters and landscape architects and horticulturists' dreams. Roads were to go here and there. The talked-about plans made no reference that I can remember to the preservation of the wild values of undisturbed Nature the arboretum already had.

Actually, the arboretum proved to be as well-administered for multiple purposes as any place of its kind of which I know. Regardless of this arboretum's man-made orderliness, its exotic plantings, and its showplace features, its special wild values were by no means forfeited to artificiality. Furthermore, plant communities that years before had been plowed up, cut away, or pastured out were restored by planting native plants, and these restorations were ingeniously carried out to simulate natural revegetation.

The nearly virgin forest may not be visited by as many people as the parts that are more easily accessible by road. It may not have as much public appeal as the colorful exotic plantings, nor as much as the formal gardens about a spring where people throw bread to a flock of tame mallards. Yet the forest remnant represents to me the most distinctive value of the arboretum.

It has been thirty years since I last visited that piece of

Journal of Wildlife Management 27(2): 313–20 (1963).

woodland, and I have forgotten much detail, but once I knew the place well. My memories are of a nesting pair of broad-winged hawks that lived mainly on the shrews and large insects of the forest floor; of great horned owls and weasels and flying squirrels; of woodpeckers and sapsuckers, nuthatches, creepers, and jays; of deer mice that climbed in bushes, of woodchucks and cottontails and striped skunks. Of holes in ground and holes in trees, of vines and hanging treetops and dead stubs, briars and saplings and shade-tolerant under-growth. It had been a place for ruffed grouse on occasion and also on occasion for that magnificent raptorial visitor from northern backwoods and wildernesses, the goshawk, a predator of singular power and aggressiveness.

In their own way the bobwhite quail of the wilder parts of the arboretum exemplified natural dramas of the arboretum as much as did anything. As a species, the bobwhite is best adapted to thrive where it has access to the grains and the more nutritious weed seeds of agricultural land; but the species is native to the region and obviously had some way of maintaining itself at biologically minimal numbers before settlement by the white man; and there in the nearly virgin forest of the arboretum, it subsisted upon the seeds of native legumes and the relatively few other foods suitable for it that occurred naturally.

There, bobwhites also could starve, as they undoubtedly had done throughout manless millenia, when the snow became deep or competition with other seed-eating forms drastically reduced whatever food remained available above the snow. There, too, bobwhites responded, as throughout the millenia, to the presence of their dreaded enemy, the Cooper's hawk. If the bobwhites had certain advantages and did the right things, they could take care of themselves; if not, they could die much as bobwhites always have died when they had to.

They jumped for the hanging trefoil pods and pecked beneath the feeding trees of squirrels. They waited out a danger by hiding in a thicket or achieved invisibility by sitting unmoving on the snow for a day and a night. They walked or ran or flew or called scattered covey members together or huddled in a circle, the whole covey of them, heads out and tail to tail. Or birds burst forth into flight with a steel-spring sound of power in the cold air and dodged through the trees with a speed and sureness proving their fitness for living their lives in the old way.

140

To see the drama of Life in its age-tested relationships is a privilege that becomes harder and harder for the human occupants of our man-crowded world to enjoy. To find places where one may even imagine Nature in an undisturbed state has become all but impossible over wider and wider areas.

One could not quite imagine even the wildest tracts of the arboretum as being wholly without the white man's influence. Nevertheless, that university arboretum was insurance that some of the natural values of one part of the country would not be lost unnecessarily nor completely.

But a disquieting thought keeps coming back to me: the recollection of a remark heard when the new plans for the arboretum were first being considered. It was just an offhand remark, disquieting because it was symptomatic of what is, in my opinion, a lack of appreciation for the values that are really priceless in our remaining out-of-doors.

The person making the remark was an admirable gentleman. He was a biologist, he loved the out-of-doors, he carried on birdbanding as a hobby, and he always could be counted on to help in any worthy conservation program or to encourage any student who might be inclined to become a naturalist.

His remark was that all of the old underbrush, dead trees, and rotten logs in that nearly virgin forest ought to be cleaned out. Although he agreeably acknowledged the rights of hole-nesting birds and flying squirrels to the dead stubs when I brought this out, I am sure that he would have been satisfied to have cut down the stubs and offered the birds and squirrels nest boxes.

If such a literate and discriminating gentleman who loved the out-of-doors and outdoor beauty could not appreciate the unique value of a tract of public-owned, undisturbed wild land on the outskirts of a fair-sized city full of conventional landscaping, what chance can there be of preserving any remnants of wilderness anywhere that man may reach and tamper with? And, if not on public-owned and public-administered lands, where can we retain any real outdoor naturalness in the usual settled community?

Man as a phenomenon can be overwhelming, even in the places he dedicates to the preservation of Nature and natural values. He may put himself to substantial trouble and expense to go on a wilderness canoe trip but be unwilling to leave even fragments of wilderness close to home, even on public lands set aside at least partially for such a purpose. Where he has control of wild lands, he seems impelled to build roads, cottages, boat docks, put in electricity, cut and clear and plant. He seems impelled to do something, somehow, that makes whatever he can reach other than what it was before.

Over vast areas of the United States and southern Canada, the remnants of natural out-of-doors that are at all in virgin, untampered condition shrink yearly until almost nothing is left. That is it. In many communities what is original and irreplaceable about Nature is gone, lost by default or by intent, piece by piece.

Furthermore, much of the destruction of really distinctive values may occur in the name of conservation. It may be carried on by conservation agencies on some of the places best suited for the preservation of distinctive values and on places where one of the responsibilities of those agencies is to preserve those values as a part of a public trust.

The United States as a nation lost a great deal through governmental relief work during the Great Depression of the thirties. The inclusion of the word *conservation* in agency names did not insure that conservation would result—nor does it today. I do not wish to imply that everything that these agencies did or do must be wrong. Some of the fire trails needed to be built, some of the bridges needed repair, maybe campgrounds were needed, maybe something else needed doing; but there certainly was enough slicking up and outright dilution of our remaining natural wildness to sicken many people who were interested in naturalness where it could be found in the out-of-doors.

I remember the sadness with which the late Aldo Leopold—one of the truly great leaders in modern conservation—told me of the artificializing of a wild area in intended behalf of game management. Log-hut feeding stations had been erected all over, with no imaginative regard for any of the more subtle values sought in recreational hunting. The only consideration was that there be game, that the game be managed like so many head of domestic stock. What was there in that, he asked, which was worth having?

One of my own recollections of misguided activity relates to a wooded peninsula extending out into a public-owned prairie lake. This peninsula probably had not changed much since the days of the Indians and the bison. It was the most delightfully wild and beautiful tract of woods and underbrush to be found for miles. It was sufficiently far from the surrounding cultivated fields and farm buildings so that one might not hear the tractors. In its depths it gave an illusion of remoteness and an intimate view of the interrelationships of living things, from the calling of young horned owls begging parents for food to the leaves of trees and shrubs contesting among themselves for the sunlight. Then somebody got in there with an axe, cut down some of the trees, and made feeding stations and shelters for the introduced ring-necked pheasants—artificial structures that even from the standpoint of pheasant management were unneeded.

Not many miles away are more public-owned lakes and surrounding lands. Some of these have their natural wild features, bur-oak woods and adjacent tracts of prairie and marsh; some do not. One lakeshore fringe of trees had a belt of prairie between it and a cultivated field, and this remnant of prairie is now represented by row after row of planted trees and shrubs. Russian olives and multiflora roses and evergreens may belong somewhere, but they are no substitute for another lost remnant of wild prairie.

Another area was acquired for a state park. As a community undertaking, acres and acres were planted to trees and shrubs, with rows of ornamentals going up and down the glacial hills. No one had thought of safeguarding what the ice sheets and the years of interactions of plants and animals and soils and climate had left. Before the planting of the ornamentals, parts of the state park had not been far from the condition in which the settlers had first found them—not quite the virgin prairie of morainal hills in a setting of glacial lakes but nearly so.

It should be emphasized as much as need be that we have very little left in untampered natural values over much of our country. Where in any fertile community in, let us say, north-central United States do we have lakes or marshes—among those that still remain undrained—with waters that are not regulated by dams or not artificially deepened by dredging? Where can people who live in this region expect to find anything wild with the sanction of a thousand years behind it? They are unlikely to find much close to home.

In central Iowa there is a state-owned glacial marsh—the only one for miles and miles. People have long been interested in it as a waterfowl marsh and have gone there, especially during spring migration, to watch the ducks and geese and associated bird life. Much of it was dredged so that its fish would not winterkill and so that the water would be deep enough for speedboating. Someone informally dumped in minnows, including the alien carp. When the multiplication of carp and their destructive activities made the marsh into more and more of a mud hole, the whole fish population had to be poisoned and a new start made. Now the plans are to pump in up to five feet of water to facilitate the speedboating, and only a few people seem to be concerned about what this will do to the vegetation of the marsh and the waterfowl migration. Maybe people just assume that they will have all they want of the vegetation and that the ducks and geese will continue to come, anyway. But, irrespective of what damage raising water levels may do to the natural values of the marsh, the vocal public pressure is for speedboating. Speedboating is what we are going to have.

There were also proposals by local irrigation interests to do something big with respect to the principal stream in our county. A system of dams five miles apart would not only provide the water for irrigation (which is a subject of much dispute) but would also furnish artificial lakes for—of course—speedboating, fishing, lots for summer cottages, and the whole array of "improvements needed to develop the recreational assets" of a community. It would, incidentally, provide some economic opportunities for persons in positions to take advantage of them. Very probably, it would give the mass-use public more of what it wants.

The woodlots that would be removed or flooded in connection with the proposed manipulations do not constitute virgin forest as they now stand. Some of the big twisted trees might date back to Revolutionary times, but most of the marketable timber—such as the choicer walnuts—has been cut, and it is usually possible to see that man has been around for some time if no more than from ravaged bee trees. However, these bottomland woods together with the stream flowing on its bed in conformity to the laws of physics have their natural values of which I do not feel scornful. Our country does not have too much left of the relatively untampered.

I do not know how far it is possible to go in analyzing the human motivations behind the excessive wastage of what have already become rarities.

144

The conquest of Nature philosophy is surely based in part upon human experience when wilderness dominated and man was weak. During hard times we can say facetiously, let's give the land back to the Indians, but whenever a census shows fewer people than the preceding one, the rallying cries of progress may exhort us to regain the spirit of the pioneers. The idea of making the desert bloom as a rose and all its variants presupposes that man has a moral right and duty to assert his mastery over the forces of raw Nature. Desert and wilderness, accordingly, are not only regarded as wasteland but as wasteland to be redeemed for the production of conventional values as much as their resources warrant.

There are the traditional concepts of neatness that determine what is acceptable to a given culture, even though traditionally acceptable practices may include the detrimental. At an extreme, a farmer may persist in plowing straight up and down hillsides instead of contouring, despite the accelerated erosion of the soil, because he thinks that straight lines are a better measure of his skill. More usually, the attitudes of the neatness cults may be manifested by what is done about the plant growths on the nonagricultural lands of a community. To allow vegetation to grow spontaneously may invite charges of shiftlessness, and it may take outstanding leadership to convince people that natural vegetation can with propriety be left undisturbed in woodlots or odd corners. A community may sanction the leaving of brush and grass along fencerows and roadsides for the birds or the leaving of a piece of natural woods or a bog because it is the habitat of a rare flower; but anything of this sort had better be specifically intended, the motives well advertised, and the effort self-evident.

It very nearly must be self-evident that someone is going to expense and trouble to give Nature her permitted chance to be spontaneous if Nature's spontaneity is going to pass the critics in possibly the average garden-club community. Somebody has to work. One cannot sit back and let all the brush and weeds give the place a low-class, run-down look. In working for the usually more socially acceptable conservation programs, planning boards must plan. Engineers must build or dredge or bulldoze. Foresters must plant and manage. In some places, gamekeepers or their counterparts must be responsible for managing the game.

My intent is not to attack the planners, engineers, foresters,

145

or gamekeepers categorically. There are individuals among them who have broad viewpoints and a reverence for values that should not be tampered with, who do not see there is necessarily anything worthless about what has taken much longer than human lifetimes to form.

Aldo Leopold was trained as a forester and spent most of his professional life in forestry, the same profession having practitioners who feel they must even plant their conifers in straight lines throughout areas set aside as nature preserves. A greatly respected man in this profession, he broke away from obsessions with planting and board feet to become one of the pioneers in modern wildlife management. He emphasized the subtle as well as the more patent values and the importance of preventing over assiduous management from impoverishing the natural outdoors.

Another forester of whom I think, this one a Swede, also is prominent in his profession. While he remains professionally engaged in forestry, he works hard at his avocation of reconciling the conflicts between forestry, game management, and nature-protection in his country. In fact, there are a great many foresters who see more to their public responsibilities than planting trees everywhere, tending forests almost like gardens, harvesting mature timber whenever and wherever it occurs, and building their own professional empires.

In a celebrated article on the esthetics of conservation, Leopold commented that we most needed to build not roads into lovely scenery but receptivity into the still unlovely human mind. Others have repeatedly expressed the thought that management of our outdoor resources in a desirable sense boils down to man management, and the truth in that is something not to be ignored. We need changes in attitudes to promote reciprocal courtesy in managing what at least on paper belongs to all of us. We need to keep aware of our decent responsibilities for those who come after us. We need, maybe from a broader, not wholly definable viewpoint, to show some deference toward the integrity of Nature.

It is true that some outdoor areas need only protection from man—such as a great redwood forest or a timberline on a mountaintop or a desert biota or a tropical rain forest. Yet preservation of the distinctive features of a natural area may also require more than just preventing human disturbance. Some of the plant and animal associations of great interest do not represent climax or end-point stages. They may require interruption of plant successions to retain their in-between character. Our virgin prairies that evolved as a resultant of fires and grazing by bison cannot be expected to continue looking as they originally did in the absence of all burning and grazing; they can choke up with old plant debris to the extent that plant and animal forms properly belonging there cannot maintain themselves. Likewise, the management of some forests may require interference with successional stages—as may marshes or some other parts of the out-of-doors that we may particularly want to save.

Rules of thumb are hard to apply with any exactitude, as a local situation may call for fire or for fire protection, interference with natural events or leaving alone; but the one rule of thumb that may be confidently advanced is to interfere as little as possible with natural events in situations where naturalness itself constitutes the supreme value.

When any interference or management is necessary for the sake of natural values, it should be done on the not wholly new principle that art conceals art. Maybe, following the art concealing art philosophy, something can be done to improve wild areas that are a long way from being virgin but have elements of natural attractiveness left.

I have in mind a small ranch in south-central Montana. It is, in the eyes of its owners, a place of exceptional natural beauty and it is adjacent to a national forest of exceptional beauty. The ranch still has to contribute to the livelihood of people. Most of the tillable land on it still has to be tilled, the hayfields kept in hay, the pastureland pastured, and the timber has to yield posts, poles, logs, and firewood as these are needed. It still has to be a producing ranch, though on a small scale. And the new cabin up on a hill well away from the original ranch buildings and the trail leading to it represent some dilution of the natural wildness of the wildest tract on the place.

The cabin, however, was built at the edge of the wild tract, and the latter was set aside to be protected from further disturbance. In an area of ten acres or so, there has been no cutting of natural growths for over a quarter-century except in the vicinity of the cabin. All timber or underbrush that dies or breaks off or falls stays in the air or on the ground, as Nature manages, according to the oldest way that things are done on Earth.

Horses, which admittedly were not there before the coming

147

of the white man to North America, do follow the trails through the preserved tract; but on a producing ranch, some lines have to be drawn somewhere, and the horses in reasonable numbers damage the natural values about as little as would any kind of livestock worth keeping. Besides, the horse trails are also game trails, and they may show more tracks of wild animals than of tame—sometimes the tracks are all of wild animals. Coyotes and porcupines and hares leave their tracks in the mud of low places. Now and then a bear walks along a game trail, and its authoritative flat heel and claw marks blot out the tracks of lesser creatures.

Or one may see the bear—big and black and minding-own-business as a wild bear should be doing—walking in a trail, walking along a hillside, or standing upright amid the June-berries. Or see the deer bounding or turning around to look. Or see a coyote, maybe hunting ground squirrels out from the edge of the woods, ears forward, ready to spring. Or find a goshawk nest. Or see broods of ruffed or blue grouse or some minor but essential creatures of foothill woods, the nutcrackers or red squirrels, or chipmunks, or something else.

The ranch was once the site of a family project in restoring naturalness where such could feasibly be done. On the wild area the stumps showing axe cuts were broken down or torn up and they as well as axe-cut branches were burned in the cabin box stove. The little trout stream flowing through a belt of as-pens and alders past the ranch buildings and the cabin was cleaned of junk that had been accumulating for decades: the bottles, cans, broken crockery, old tires, old clothes, old boards, old stoves, and bedsprings, the axe-cut brush that hardly added to the naturalness of the stream.

The family project did include a little tinkering with rocks and the creek bottom to deepen pools and create riffles and deflect the current in ways that might be more favorable to the trout; but such tinkering was done in ways to suggest that gla-cial ice and subsequent freshets had done it naturally long ago. The cutting and damming by the rightful population of beavers was not interfered with at all.

The project, with no visible detriment to the productivity of the ranch and with no cash outlay, resulted in a fair-sized na-ture preserve, a block of native foothill forest with a stream going through it in a setting of more conventional ranchland.

The national forest itself is by no means wholly virgin. It

has cuttings, irrigation dams, ski runs, campgrounds, cabins along a major stream. Nevertheless, far up in the canyon of the creek and up across mountain ridges and up other canyons, the forest has wilderness. High enough and remote enough live martens, and I have seen big-cat tracks that looked like lynx tracks. There are some grizzly bears, a few cougars, and there might be, rarely, a wolverine. Moose range away up past timberline, and wapiti herds live in the valleys and on the slopes they like. Beavers, minks, marmots, conies, the deer and the coyotes, golden eagles, nearly a dozen species of hawks, four kinds of grouse from the mouth of the creek to the beginning, ptarmigans up high, the chipmunks and red squirrels, packrats and deer mice—so many may be listed. Horned owls hoot and live their own lives as birds of prey, whether feeding upon grouse and hares or gorging upon army worms.

Down below, the small tract with the horse trails and the cleaned-up stream may be regarded as especially valuable from the standpoint of preserving Nature in nearly undisturbed condition in between the pushing human population and the more majestic part of the national forest. The small tract has nothing to compare with the beautiful expanse of mountain wilderness but it is something, of itself, a remnant of foothill wilderness of a type that can disappear, too—into pastures, real estate developments, or something else not resembling wild Nature. It has its own integrity.

As I see it, we do not need an elaborate code to guide us in the preservation of the values that are not man-made, the natural values that are nearly gone everywhere that man lives, and the values that we cannot replace.

Just the simple criterion of what belongs naturally in an untampered, undefiled wild place should suffice. Basically that can be simple. Or it can be expressed in terms of recognition of what the preservation of Nature does *not* need. It does not need more evidence of man or man's tampering everywhere that one may look. That much could be thought of before the nursery trucks, the bulldozers, the draglines, and the work crews appear in those last few places that particularly should be left alone.

149

OF MAN AND THE LAWS OF LIFE

"OF MAN AND THE LOWER ANIMALS" WAS published in the Yale Review *in 1962 as a request article. It is a restatement of the epilogue to* Of Men and Marshes, *published by Macmillan in 1957. Subsequently it was reprinted in* The Subversive Science: Essays toward an Ecology of Man, *by Paul Shepard and Daniel McKinley, Houghton Mifflin Company, 1964.*

Years before Paul wrote "Of Man and the Lower Animals" he had been watching with apprehension the unprecedented increase in the world's population; and he saw in the demographic figures much more to be alarmed about than the possibility of man outrunning his food supply. In this essay he asks: "What, specifically, could civilized man learn from population phenomena of the so-called lower animals that might help him understand population phenomena of his own kind? What, specifically, might help him in his seeking for 'the better life' "? He answers those two questions in this essay without drawing any unjustified parallels.

WORK ON A GLACIAL MARSH WHERE NATIVE
WILD CREATURES LIVED IN FREEDOM.
Photo by Marion Ferguson

Of Man and the Lower Animals

AN IS A MOST SPECIAL ANIMAL. HOWEVER much disagreement may exist as to his origin or purpose (if any), we can agree that he has both simplified and complicated his way of living and has made a great impact on his surroundings. The phenomenon of man, whether we think of it with exultation or despair or with some emotion in between, remains strong stuff and has prospects of getting stronger. Man may fancy himself exempt from natural laws or well on the way toward becoming so; his technological advances seem to promote delusions as to what he is and can do.

Man can, on at least some logical grounds, rate himself as a higher animal. He has already named himself the wise, *Homo sapiens,* and he can at times show capabilities for wisdom. He is special, but he should not assume that he is higher, wiser, or more special than he is. An unrealistic attitude of man toward himself as an animal can be, I think, most dangerous. If twentieth-century society really values the things that it proclaims essential to a civilized culture—peace, human dignity, intellectual activity, a reasonable degree of freedom and security, and a reasonable standard of living—it cannot afford to ignore the natural laws by which life continues to be bound.

It is particularly when thinking about the increase of human beings over the habitable areas of the Earth that I am afraid not only for man's physical future but also for the values that go furthest toward making human life worth living.

I confess to further disquieting thoughts as to how much moral right man actually has to regard the Earth as his exclusive possession, to despoil or befoul as he will. Man has or should have some minimal responsibility toward the Earth he claims and toward the other forms of life that have been on Earth as long as or longer than he has.

Yale Review 51(3):370–83 (1962).

Public attitudes toward the recent, current, and future increase of the Earth's human populations may hardly be summarized briefly or neatly. People may joke that the so-called population explosion will not matter to any of us a hundred years hence. Or Providence or scientific gadgetry will save us, if we are to be saved. Or the attitude may be that the Earth could support many times its present human population and that the era of human colonization of other worlds in space awaits us; and that continued population growth is necessary to assure us of anything rightly identifiable with progress. But whether the public view is that of fatalists caught in an irresistible current or of boosters convinced that not even the sky need be the limit, seldom is any evidence to be detected that the public knows much about populations, about its own or any other populations. Seemingly it should be appropriate for the public, as participating in this great increase, to concern itself more with what it is doing, afraid of, or aiming for.

This essay proposes no panaceas. It is mainly to develop the by-no-means novel thesis that man could learn from consideration of the basic biology and sociology of animal populations.

The population dynamics of man and what man calls lower animals may not show detailed parallels throughout. The life equation of modern man can be subject to an all but unending array of qualifying conditions. Within the framework of the laws of life, he can be a breaker as well as a maker of rules. He is a product of diverse cultures and blends of cultures and offshoots of cultures. He may be as intolerant of crowding as an American frontiersman who wanted no neighbors in sight or as tolerant as a metropolitan to whom crowds represent a normal environment. He may demand and be sensitively adjusted to a high standard of living. He may be materialistic when having much or philosophical when in want. Man is venturesome and conservative, patient and volatile, reasoning and unreasoning.

If man is to learn anything about populations of lower animals so that he may better understand his own populations, it may just about have to be at the more elementary levels. This might not impress some who feel that we need more than an elementary understanding. We do need understanding on the highest plane that we can reach, but I feel that we can ill afford to be scornful about what we can learn that is elementary as long as we as a public continue to demonstrate so little understanding of that. If man knew more about population fundamentals, I doubt if he would so blindly make certain of the mistakes that he does make.

A tremendous amount of work has been done in following the population fortunes of wild mammals and birds living their own lives under more or less natural conditions. The work has been chiefly on game birds, songbirds, fur bearers, and rodent pests; and their habits and vital statistics have been recorded for the same tracts of land year after year and discussed in the biological literature for a quarter-century or longer.

My research specialities among these species have included two native North Americans: the bobwhite quail and the muskrat. They both illustrate population resiliences and rigidities concerning which misconceptions may persist.

Some of the most misleading of misconceptions relate to food as a limiting factor of populations. Granted that some species of animals do increase up to the limits of their food supply; that animals must eat and if they do not get enough to eat, they may starve; or that populations may otherwise decline because of food deficiencies; it may still be an unsafe assumption that the upper limits of a population must necessarily be determined by lack of food, or, for that matter, by lack of other palpable environmental constituents that we customarily think of as limiting factors.

Not so very many years ago the wintering fortunes of bobwhite populations in the north-central and north-eastern United States were considered almost exclusively in terms of weather, natural enemies, food, and cover.

It is true that severe weather emergencies may now and then practically eliminate the bobwhite as a species over wide areas of its geographic range. Two feet of heavy snow or an inch-thick seal of ice over everything for a couple of weeks or longer may pose their understandable threats to susceptible wildlife. So may twenty to forty below zero temperatures accompanied by blizzard winds and eight-foot snowdrifts. Yet a given area—a whole region—may not have any weather emergencies of lethal intensity for bobwhites for years, and, even so, the bobwhite populations tend to increase up to a certain level and no higher.

The thesis that bobwhites are limited in numbers and distribution by the depredations of flesh-eating enemies has long been a public favorite. Predatory flesh eaters do kill and eat bobwhites about as often as they have opportunities, and they may have many or conspicuous opportunities to do so. Nevertheless, this predation, when closely studied, has proved to be more a symptom of insecurity in a wintering bobwhite population than a primary limiting factor.

The food and cover—those essential constituents of wintering environment for the bobwhites—must be present when, where, and in the quantity and quality and combinations needed, or the birds cannot long live anywhere. But excess food or cover is unlikely to be accompanied by any corresponding increase in numbers of the bobwhites that are able to winter. The chief limiting factor becomes the psychology of the bobwhites themselves.

Such a population picture does not have its fully traceable counterparts throughout the animal kingdom. Psychological intolerances do not always prevent increases up to levels where food does become the limiting factor—as in those insects the abundance of which is governed by food supply and in those human populations to whom subsistence living and starvation are commonplace. It does apply, however, to that wide variety of mammals and birds that we think of as being territorial, those we classify as the property owners, those making claims that they are willing to defend. This territoriality is manifested by the fights and displays of songbirds settling their rights of possession on a city lawn and by some remarkably humanlike behavior. An animal's own psychological intolerance toward its own kind can be a mighty factor in determining what lives where, when, how, and at what densities.

Another distinction emphasized by the bobwhite data: although there can be fighting (including fighting between social groups that may not be dissimilar to human warfare), the limiting factor of social intolerance need not always take the form of overt antagonism or fighting. Some of the most significant intolerance can have such benign bird-between-bird manifestations as frictionless avoidance or withdrawals on the part of individuals or groups that recognize their own superfluity in places where they do not belong.

Even so, manifestations of social overpopulation can include plenty of trouble. Bobwhite equivalents of displaced persons wander in strange places or try to live in uninhabitable areas. In their wanderings they tend to be harassed by and vulnerable to predatory attacks. Not only may they be vulnerable to such formidable predators as great horned owls and dashing blue-darter hawks and agile and clever foxes but also to rather weak and clumsy predators having no special aptitudes for preying upon grown bobwhites unless something goes wrong. To a considerable extent it may not seem to make much difference what kills the birds that are trying to live under highly adverse, if not hopeless, conditions. They are the have-nots and they do not need to have human intelligence to know it. They may lack food or cover; they may lack both; but possibly as contributory as anything to their serious troubles, they lack what might be called the sense of rightness that enables them to do the best they can with what they have.

Not only are wanderers affected but also those among an area's wintering bobwhites that are relatively sedentary but trying to live at too-high densities for peace and security, even as bobwhites know peace and security. This may be true in places having far more than sufficient food and cover for all the bobwhites that conceivably would ever live or visit there. One can see it about an Iowa cornfield having tons of the best all-around food for wintering bobwhites and lying conveniently adjacent to a woodlot full of the best of refuge cover for the birds—a place having food enough to feed thousands and cover enough to afford mechanical protection to hundreds, but having only perhaps thirty to forty birds that act as if they know when they are enough.

Long-term data on bobwhite populations of Iowa and Wisconsin have tendencies to line up with remarkable fidelity to numerical patterns, often for many consecutive years. For a period of years not more than a fairly definite number of bobwhites would be able to winter on a given tract of land under the best weather conditions, and the numbers trying to live there in excess of that figure would soon be whittled down by predation or be forced to leave or would withdraw of their own volition. After elimination of the vulnerable surplus, the remaining bobwhites would stand a good chance of wintering securely, despite the presence and activities of native enemies that would be entirely willing to feed upon them if they could do so. In the event that the bobwhite population entered the winter and stayed at a level well below the threshold of security, those particular birds might not suffer any wintering loss or only the trifling losses that might occur through age or accident.

An actual case history for a tract of about a thousand acres demonstrated a threshold of security at about fifty bobwhites for the six winters that I made detailed observations. During one winter of heavy snowfall this tract had the best food supply in the whole neighborhood and it was repeatedly visited by hungry quail coveys from outside its boundaries. Each such visit resulted in the local population exceeding the threshold of security for the thousand-acre tract and, unless extremely temporary, was followed by a reduction down to the threshold level, until the birds losing their lives there outnumbered the even fifty that did survive.

Differences in the wintering fortunes of secure and insecure populations may show up in still greater contrast. Another six-year case history relates to a covey range that was rich in food though lethally poor in protective cover and a site of chronic unrest for the quail whenever any lived there. For the five winters of the six that it attracted quail, it wintered two birds out of a total of eighty-four. About a third of the decline was due to birds abandoning the tract while alive and able to do so. The rest of the decline occurred through predation. For the season that the two birds wintered, virtually the whole loss of twenty-one was traced to a pair of great horned owls. Yet in the center of the nesting territory of the owls, thirty-two of thirty-two bobwhites wintered. Another neighboring but strong and well-balanced covey range wintered thirty-three without a single loss. Elsewhere in the same neighborhood during the same winter, the two other covey ranges nearest the scene of the practically annihilative predation lost six birds out of thirty-nine, which represented just about the elimination of a vulnerable surplus on the range of these birds.

In detailed analysis, the story of what happens at times of a bobwhite population crisis can become too involved to discuss in a short article, but I want to emphasize the social intolerance underlying so much of the trouble associated with overpopulation. There need not be any overt friction manifested even when the appearance of newcomers puts a population dangerously over the threshold of security that applies to a given tract of wintering range. Newcomers may even join with resident "homesteaders," roosting tail to tail in a common circle. But uneasiness and the preoccupation of birds with each other may divert attention from the proper business of living, whether in getting along well or in staying alive at all.

The apparent role of food as a limiting factor in muskrat

populations may differ with the area and with the subspecies of muskrat. In the coastal marshes of Maryland and Louisiana (which comprise two population centers for southern forms of muskrats), the animals may eat themselves out of their habitats in the accepted Malthusian sense. Conversely, the population increases of the muskrats studied in Iowa were almost invariably damped before the onset of frankly Malthusian stages.

Nor does the mechanism basically limiting the population growth of the Iowa muskrats especially conform to the Darwinian version of the balance of nature. It has nothing that I can see of predation any more than it has of Malthusian-type food limitation working as a master factor to remove enough of the annual production of muskrats to keep populations within bounds—despite the fact that predation upon vulnerable parts of populations may be heavy. On areas where predatory enemies were virtually absent (or did little or no preying upon the muskrats), the muskrats did not show an unrestrained increase.

The reproductive changes shown by the Iowa muskrats have been particularly informative. Average numbers of young conceived by or born to adult females of given populations during a given year varied from about a dozen young up to about three times that many. Generally, the average litter size may reflect more the health and nourishment of the females, whereas the average number of litters born per adult female during a breeding season may more reflect the collective dispositions or states of mind or social tensions of the population or maybe something else not so satisfactorily labeled.

A changing birth rate in a muskrat population does not have to signify any genetic change, nor any irreversible trend either up or down. Change may be expected whenever biological conditions induce change. Broadly, when social tensions increase, the birth rate falls; when tensions are relieved, the birth rate rises.

The adult females in overcrowded muskrat populations typically stop breeding after giving birth to averages of about two litters. This would be about the first of June in Iowa, in the middle of the breeding season shown by the calendar. The mere presence of many young underfoot or sneaking around or getting into trouble or being a distracting influence in the sociology of the population seems to inhibit further breeding.

The weaned young of uncrowded populations have better

159

opportunities for dispersing away from the properties of their elders and not only spare themselves trouble but also reduce their own chances of causing trouble. Populations that do not have their breeding production inhibited by the presence of excessive numbers of young might give birth to averages approaching four litters per adult female for the season, or about twice the average for the crowded populations.

Or, crowded populations suffering heavy losses of their early born young (as through late spring and early summer floods drowning most of the young born before midsummer) might give birth to additional, late litters in compensation for the loss of the earlier ones. Death may thus serve the biological function of a moderate degree of underpopulation insofar as it similarly results in lowered social tensions, at least to the extent of there being fewer young to be getting in the way of their elders and thus inhibiting reproduction.

The commonly held supposition that fecund animals need their fecundity to outbreed their heavy loss rates, to keep ahead of their enemies, or to compete with their fellows should not be accepted without question.

Case histories of muskrat populations do show how animals producing the larger numbers of young stand better chances of filling up underpopulated habitats with their own progeny. Following droughts, for example, the return of surface water may put the lakes and marshes of a whole region in superior condition for muskrats at a time when only a few muskrats may be present to live in them. Muskrats thus living in places characterized by splendid resources and minimal social tensions may rear nearly all of the young born to them; and in the accelerating stages of a population rise, a breeding season's production of young may show such impressive results as averages exceeding twenty young successfully reared per adult female. That would occur when the animals would be sufficiently abundant to have full opportunities for mating yet still be below the levels of crowding at which the psychological brakes start tightening.

Once the muskrats fill up their habitat, they do not need a high reproductive rate to keep their population at a capacity level. Even the lower birth rates shown by the Iowa muskrats— such as an average of a dozen young born per adult female— ordinarily are sufficient to replenish a population; and the survival rate of these young need not be especially high.

160

For a crowded population beset by much social tension, averages as low as four young successfully reared per female may be all that can be expected even when nothing goes seriously wrong with the habitat. Such a reproductive rate would be attained through rearing an average of half the young born in a single litter per adult female. The relatively slow breeders can still have all the fecundity they need to hold a population at a saturated level, especially in view of the fact that an adult female almost always takes better care of a few young than she does of many young.

Some of the postulated biological advantages of high fecundity therefore cancel out as social tensions build up. For a population that cannot withstand crowding and has no more livable frontiers to spread into, greater fecundity can mean greater wastage.

The natural shaking down of the muskrat population to fit its habitat and its social mold may be bloodily messy, even when the only deadly muskrat enemies are other muskrats. Compared with the troubles of many other species, muskrat troubles may have more savage violence in them if only because the muskrats possess murderous teeth and dispositions commensurate with the teeth whenever social conditions become intolerable. When matters really go wrong for the muskrats, all their nightmares come true.

Excess or misfit or strange adults may circulate about a marsh, finding trouble and making trouble. They may have gashes around their rumps or tails bitten through. They may have bites into kidneys, bites into livers, intestines, or into any body parts that teeth can reach and penetrate. They may try to walk on elbows after having had forelegs hamstrung. They may have face wounds, feet swollen out of shape from wounds, and wounds that fill with maggots or provide sites of bulging abscesses. They hobble around and sit in improvised nests on shore or ice; they bleed where they go and where they rest; and now and then one dies.

Strife victims may include huge animals of either sex at the height of physical prowess but not able or disposed to live in peace. They may include sick or injured or simply those too immature to take good care of themselves, the animals that could not keep away from other animals that did not want them around. Some victims may be among the aggressively troublesome; some may be only those offering inviting targets for the abuse of their fellows—the timid, the hesitant, the blundering.

A weaned young enters its home lodge and eats the hindquarters off a member of a new-born litter that it finds unprotected. A mother kills a couple of her own weaned young in driving them away before the birth of another litter. A mother may see a young muskrat swimming on the far side of the cleared space surrounding her lodge, swim out to it, and bite it to death with the utmost viciousness. Or a mother on a crowded marsh may enter a lodge containing another mother's young, kill them in the nest, and take over the lodge for the housing of her own young.

Life can be very cheap among the muskrats of an overpopulated area. In addition to the young victims that are murdered outright, many young die as a result of parental carelessness when the parents have no reason to be careful. Members of a single helpless litter have been found left lying around in as many as four different lodges. It not infrequently happens that a litter may be divided and the parts kept in nest chambers of two different lodges fifty yards or farther apart; and when this happens, the mother sometimes neglects the occupants of one of the nests, and they do not grow any more.

With increased distractions, mothers become increasingly forgetful of the numbers and whereabouts of their helpless young. When litters are being moved under pressure, a mother may carry two or three to a safe place. She may casually retrieve another young or two if she swims past them and they are complaining. Ultimately, she may gather together half her litter, and, if so, that may be enough to satisfy her. She still has young muskrats to look after, and her type of mass production does not call for exacting standards of motherhood.

The mistake should not be made of taking for granted that such troubled lives are merely the ordained lot of muskrat flesh, or that the troubles of muskrats increase in direct proportion to the numbers of the muskrats. The troubles increase out of all proportion to the numbers of muskrats as populations become top-heavy in terms of what muskrats recognize as crowding. In the other direction, lowering of populations down to levels that the muskrats find socially more tolerable means proportionally much less trouble.

This is not to say that muskrat (or bobwhite or any other) populations that contain naturally irascible individuals ever live in idyllic peace, at any population levels. There are always the aged, the ailing, the unlucky, the misfit, and their dispositions need not be of mellow contentment. Nevertheless, it is generally basic behavior for a mammal or bird population to live more peaceably when it feels that things are right than when it is subject to endless stress.

What, specifically, could civilized man learn from population phenomena of the so-called lower animals that might help him understand population phenomena of his own kind? What, specifically, might help him in his seeking for "the better life"?

In their essential features, the lessons from the lower animals look rather simple. I shall not try to say how many of them reflect anything really new philosophically. Many of them look like homely truths, and whether or not they are of sorts thinking people have always thought about, I know they are not original with me.

A frequently quoted passage from Isaiah reads: "Woe unto them that join house to house, that lay field to field, till there be no place, that they may be placed alone in the midst of the earth!" The ancients had some experience with frustrations, too, and not all of the problems in their lives were manifested by shortages of food.

The modern concepts of "pathological togetherness" as a population phenomenon seem to have developed chiefly in connection with recent work on physiological and psychological stress.

The lessons of the lower animals could help us get rid of naivetés concerning fundamentals. We could recognize that there may be more to meeting a population problem than increasing the production or improving the distribution of food or other material goods. There are the estimates as to how many times the present world population could be fed if we could make more efficient use of the resources of the sea, if algae could be adapted for human diet, if we could accomplish technological miracles in mass-producing foods without soil, and so on and so on. To me, this reasoning neglects some of the most serious problems of overpopulations, the social evils.

We could do well in getting away from misconceptions as to the biological significance of changes in birth rates. A declining birth rate should not be regarded as a calamity to be avoided by all possible means. It may be a symptom of something being wrong without being menacing in itself—indeed, it may be, of itself, exactly what is needed to better a situation.

For all of the boom talk about space travel and the unlimited horizons awaiting mankind's expansion, it might, for the present, befit human intelligence to think more about the world we still happen to be living in and filling up so rapidly with people and their by-products. What ultimate billions do we expect our populations to reach, according to a booster philosophy of always bigger and bigger? What, with such a philosophy, are we committing ourselves to?

I think that it would be more befitting human intelligence for man to take for granted that his population growth curve will level off sometime, however much he may postpone it by his technological ingenuity. Moreover, if a top-heavy human population collapses through a cataclysm instead of merely leveling off, what are the limits to which mass desperation may not go, on a scale such as our earth could never experience before it had the billions of people to become involved?

Apart from any threat—distant or not, as the case may be—of actual collapse in our population structure, the present pyramiding stage produces enough trouble and prospects of more trouble at best. Puerto Rico, the South Pacific, Africa, the metropolitan congestions that we already have in North America—we do not have to look to the congestions of Old World cultures for dismaying examples of evils associated with mankind's overpopulations. I confidently expect the troublous aspects of our population situation to be compounded the higher our numbers go, until the laws of Life absolutely put a stop to further increase.

This much is from the lower animals: the upper asymptote of a population growth curve almost always represents forced retrenchment, and the forcing represents suffering for the living forms possessed of enough nervous system to suffer. The upper asymptotes for the animals I have studied operated through no mysteriously benign process of falling birth rates; they reflected a tightening up of many things, including, especially, psychological tensions. There is no reason I can see that man, with his capacities for irascibility and suffering, could have an upper asymptote forced on his population curve without expecting intensification of the tensions that add nothing to any legacy of human happiness.

Man, as well as the lower animals, has plenty in his collective and individual destinies that he cannot expect ever to control, but it seems ironical that he cannot do better than the lower animals in at least seeing the menace in irresponsible increase.

There may well be questions as to exactly where dangers lie, as to what man can hope to do about his population problems, as to what practical measures he could take or be ethically justified in taking. At any rate, he could break away from the fallacy that his enormous population increase must necessarily be identified with progress.

If the lower animals have any one, simple, major lesson for us, it would seem to be that moderation is, or is the nearest approach to, a biological basis for any kind of "good life." The idea that adaptable mankind may be able to adapt to a new, crowded, tightly integrated, superlatively artificialized way of living still does not answer questions as to why this way of living should be a goal so desired, so worthy of attainment. Surely we have what it takes to fill the Earth with people to its habitable limits, but why must we if we can possibly avoid it?

For what goals should we be willing to allow our numbers to increase up to the point where we have less and less worth living for? More dangers of appalling political and economic dislocations? Speeded-up complexities and frantic entertainment, even the search for peace of mind at a breathless tempo, instead of more wholesome ways of living? Countrysides that are no longer in the country, opportunities to enjoy solitudes existing only farther and farther away from home, if there?

With the intelligence that man has in him, why must he in the face of danger signals give obeisance to the shaky doctrine that his population growth must never cease? Why not some goals that leave for man some of the things worth living for, not just imposing statistics or material necessities or universal gadgetry? Why, before it becomes too late, can we not at least try to do what is within our capabilities to hold our populations within some reasonable limits?

Ultimately live on algae? I suppose so if that is what we must do, but why must we as rational beings get ourselves into the position of having to do it? Dream dreams about conquering space? I suppose that it would be considered reactionary to discourage that, but first we might concern ourselves with not making a complete mess of our heritage on Earth. A philosophy of conscientious husbandry should be consistent with a civilized and progressive attitude.

ADDENDA

THE FOLLOWING DEDICATION AND TWO articles were written in praise of Arthur Karr Gilkey and Aldo Leopold.

Arthur Gilkey died in 1953 at the age of 27 on Mount Godwin-Austen in Pakistan. He had been our friend for almost fifteen years. The dedication honoring him was in Of Men and Marshes, *published by Macmillan in 1957. "An Iowa Boyhood," published in the* Iowan *9(4):43–44 (1961), is an account of our friendship.*

Aldo Leopold, the great conservationist, died in spring of 1948 while fighting a prairie fire in Sand County, Wisconsin, near the now-famous Leopold "shack." "In Appreciation of Aldo Leopold" was written the following summer and published in the Journal of Wildlife Management *12(4):341–49(1948). The article contains a careful appraisal of Leopold's career as a professional in the field of wildlife management as well as a tribute to Leopold, our friend.*

THE SMALL WESTERN RANCH WHERE
"IN APPRECIATION OF ALDO LEOPOLD" WAS WRITTEN.

To the memory of
ARTHUR KARR GILKEY, PH. D.
Boulder, Colorado, September 25, 1926
Mount Godwin-Austen, Pakistan, August 10, 1953

To a man of civilized ethics, manners, and scholarship,
yet one who loved wilderness, too.

To a man of self-direction and discipline
who loved freedom, too.

To a man of strong friendships who loved solitude, too.

To a man who loved the natural out-of-doors, whether of
marshes or of mountains, for itself and for its own values,
for its drama of the living and the nonliving, and for the
peace that it gave him.

To an admirable man and a beloved friend.

168

An Iowa Boyhood

I FIRST MET ARTHUR GILKEY, WITHOUT THEN KNOWING his name, one Saturday afternoon in the late thirties.

A Cub Scout den mother in our Ames neighborhood had found herself with more boys than she knew what to do with, and Carolyn, my wife, volunteered my help in taking them on an outing.

We went out along Squaw Creek, northwest of town, where the Cubs might see winter bird life, tracks in the snow, and the willow cuttings of a beaver colony. They could learn to read sign and appreciate the natural out-of-doors.

As the boys left the two automobiles out at the creek, I immediately thought of the hero in a Norwegian fairy tale whose assigned task had been to round up and bring home the hares of a forest, every one of them. Through the woods, up on the hillsides, down on the creek ice, outward and onward, the yelling Cubs dispersed.

In this scene of almost total horseplay, a youngster slightly older than the others walked with me and talked. He was a nice kid and helped make the afternoon passably endurable. Upon reporting to Carolyn, I learned that this boy must have been the den chief, Arthur Gilkey.

A week or two later, Art appeared at our house, bringing with him another youngster of his own age. This introduction successfully accomplished, more youngsters were brought over and individually introduced. All were in their early teens and all were interested in out-door pursuits. Ultimately, Carolyn and I had five young visitors coming over regularly, in various combinations.

Originally, they had asked mostly about birds of prey, and insofar as certain of my earlier professional studies had been of these birds, I was able to encourage the boys to follow up this interest. While still in high school they proved the incubation period of the great horned owl and published upon it in a leading ornithological journal (*Auk* 60:272–73 [1943]).

As they entered college their interests in the natural out-of-doors and its wildlife became more diversified. They worked and traveled in the mountainous West; they became skillful at woodcraft. Also, they did what they could during wartime by joining the Navy; and they began planning for their professional training.

Meanwhile, there were several years when they spent a considerable proportion of their weekends with me somewhere in the central Iowa out-of-doors. We went together on field trips in connection with the studies of animal populations that constituted my principal work at Iowa State University—and we did much midwinter rabbit hunting as soon as the boys became experienced enough to handle firearms safely.

In thinking of these boys growing up, I often think of the enthusiasm with which they could plan and go through with undertakings requiring purpose and effort. I think of their attitude toward living and what might be called "development of their intellectual resources" so much in contrast with the bored seeking after diversion and the dull, dull outlook that can be a part of youth that does not know what to do. This article, however, is about Art Gilkey rather than his close friends, even though his friends were, in a sense, inseparable from his own character and personality. It is about Art because Art's body lies under the tons of avalanche debris that killed him high up on the Himalayan peak known formally as Mount Godwin-Austen, and to mountaineers as K2.

In summer of 1948 Carolyn and two small boys were watching for him from a hilltop. I saw him as I glanced out of our cabin window. There he was, a mile away, over on the far side of the canyon; and I knew that it had to be Art as soon as I saw a man walking in our direction. Months before, all of us had planned to get together in mountainous southern Montana. Art would be a student at the Princeton Geology Camp near Red Lodge, and we would be staying at our ranch cabin, within sight of the Princeton camp.

That Sunday he walked along a gentle canyon slope and down out of sight in a wooded creek valley. Finding a crossing, he came in sight on our side of the creek. At last he came running up over the hill to the cabin with an eight-year-old Errington boy on his back. He had been keeping in condition by distance running and showed it, the mile-high altitude, and the hot sun and his load notwithstanding.

Art was by then very much grown up. He had completed his naval service; he was within a year of graduating Phi Kappa Phi from Iowa State University; and he had a good start in training for his professional field, geology.

From the time we first knew him in his early teens, he had always been a remarkably well-mannered, considerate, and responsive youth; now we could enjoy his company as a young adult who had the confidence of experience and accomplishment. We enjoyed his quiet way of talking, his quiet and mature humor, and his continued enthusiasm for what he was doing. And we so much enjoyed just being at ease, like the old friends that we really were, with this fine young man who was our guest for a day and a night.

In the evening Art and I took a walk in the foothills to listen for coyotes. Coming back, lighting the tricky places in the trail with a flashlight, we surprised a porcupine at a toolshed in the ranch yard. At least, that is how I recall it, but I cannot be entirely sure.

I am no longer sure of other memories concerning Art, but I cannot say that this makes overmuch difference to me. There is much left to remember him by, memories that come easily if in no particular order except as one thought or reminder may touch off something else.

I remember what a loyal kid he was and always so willing to be helpful. I remember him from "rabbit-cleaning parties" after a hunt; from "shell-loading parties," when, during the wartime unavailability of sporting ammunition for civilians, we handloaded the shotgun shells we had to have if we were to do any more hunting.

I remember some of the triumphs of the boys, Art among them. One of them distracted with movements a tiny saw-whet owl while another sneaked behind and grabbed it as it sat in a thicket; they brought it in for me to see before releasing it with a band marker on its leg. They photographed a litter of fox pups playing outside a den. They tested equipment for winter camping by sleeping outdoors in sleeping bags. One night the temperature dropped to thirty below zero while they slept out.

My recollections of Art here again tend to include his group of companions. That, I suppose, should be expected, considering the group.

I do have a most personal memory of Art alone: of the time he told me of having had to overcome a fear of high places in preparation for the mountaineering at which he became su-

171

perlatively expert. Before then, I would not have guessed that he ever had been afraid of anything that could be surmounted by human character.

I never did know exactly how he regarded things that were beyond human control. Probably he appraised his chances dispassionately and went ahead living his life as he best saw it, anyway.

For Art, the mountaineering represented both professional training and activity and a great love in itself. His geological specialties were those in which mountaineering skills would be invaluable, but I suspect that he chose those specialties to some extent in order to find more opportunities for mountaineering. As one who has no inclination whatever to engage in difficult mountain climbing, I do not know whether I am capable of understanding how Art felt toward the more personal of the challenges offered by mountain climbing. On the other hand, I know that I understand his feelings toward beauties that are not man-made, toward the clean air and the wonderful solitude of truly wild places, toward the chill of shadow and the warmth of sunshine away up high. I can understand the delight that he could take in an athlete's physical condition, in being a man wholly alive.

I do not think that Art took chances in his mountaineering—that is, apart from the hazards inherent in such activities. After climbing Devil's Tower, he wrote me that the climb had been safe. For him, with his physique, self-control, and know-how, I have little doubt that it had been safe. Art's death on dangerous K2 did not result from any lack of human preparation or skill. Of course, K2 would not have killed Art if he had not been on it.

In thinking of him, I do not overlook the sadness in the fact that what he loved brought about his death. The tragedy was of overwhelming finality beside which words can become meaningless, but it remains true that, while he had it to live, Art's way of life had been worth having and worth living for.

In Appreciation of Aldo Leopold

PROFESSOR ALDO LEOPOLD, CHAIRMAN OF THE DEPART-
ment of Wildlife Management of the University of Wisconsin
and a past-president of the Wildlife Society, died of a heart attack near his summer home at Baraboo, Wisconsin, April 21,
1948, after two hours of fighting a bad grass fire on a neighbor's
land.

I shall not here write of his personal life except in relation to
his career in the professional field of wildlife management.

It is proper that he be singled out for the attention of the
profession's members. Without belittling in any way his numerous contemporaries, it may be said that he, more than anyone
else, has been responsible for the expansion and refinement of
wildlife management as such is known today. As a measure of
this, we need only consider the strategic positions he held, the
astounding amount of work he did on committees, the insight
and diligence with which he pioneered in the field, his honesty
of purpose, and his inspiring and leading of youngsters and the
mature alike. At a conference a couple of years ago he was introduced as a speaker with the words, "Dean of Deans" of the
profession, which might have sounded trite if applied to
another, yet for him seemed wholly appropriate.

I met Aldo in the spring of 1929, when he was conducting a
game survey of the north-central United States for the Sporting
Arms and Ammunition Manufacturers' Institute. He was likewise the institute's representative for a series of graduate research fellowships on game birds it was financing at land-grant
universities. I held one of these fellowships for three years, beginning July 1929, and it happened to be with the University of
Wisconsin at Madison—also the city of the Leopold home and
office. As Aldo was not appointed to the University of Wisconsin
staff until 1933 (a year after I had left the campus), I was never
formally his student.

Informally, I moved in on him, his home, and his library for
hours at a stretch, talking "shop" or anything else. I wasn't a

restful satellite and sometimes argued in an evening until neither of us could sleep long after going to bed, but he was gracious toward me and patient with my ex-trapper's social deficiencies. And he was kindly insistent that, as concerned complex natural phenomena like animal fluctuations, one should first gather an abundance of facts to study rather than put forth opinions based chiefly or solely upon outdoor experience.

He appreciated the ability and scientific outlook of H. L. Stoddard and W. L. McAtee (notably as manifested by the southeastern researches on bobwhites and associated species), of Charles Elton, the British ecologist, of the late P. S. Lovejoy of Michigan, and of creative thinkers wherever he found them, in person or through their publications. He was one of the first in the field really to see the exceptional virtues and promise of the untalkative young Franklin J. W. Schmidt, who died in a fire just as his work on central Wisconsin prairie chickens was becoming recognized.

Aldo's own alertness and powers of synthesis were evident from the beginning of my relations with him. Even when beset by great fatigue, he could somehow continue to think effectively. To me, one of his most impressive intellectual performances was during hospitalization for an unrecalled ailment: under stimulus of an impending deadline, he dictated whole chapters of his "Report of a Game Survey of the North Central States," published by the institute in 1931. Later, he was characteristically dissatisfied with its loose ends, but irrespective of these, it stands as a remarkable achievement.

In retrospect, I think not only of his personal qualities as of the time when I knew him best, but also of his virtually undertaking, at middle age, a new profession and making this his distinguished life work after what are commonly a man's most plastic and productive years.

Aldo was born on January 11, 1887, at Burlington, Iowa, and became interested in ornithology and hunting during boyhood and youth along the Mississippi River. He was trained in forestry at Yale, receiving the degree of Master of Forestry in 1909. Thereupon, he entered the U.S. Forest Service as a forest assistant and worked with the organization in southwestern United States until 1924, meanwhile rising through several grades to that of chief of operations.

If we look over the first dozen titles (1916–1919) in the Leopold bibliography compiled by J. J. Hickey (University of

Wisconsin Wildlife Research News Letter, no. 35, May 3, 1948), we may see that his earlier publications were much like those any able young field naturalist might write. They were mostly notes in the *Condor* and a couple of papers on game in the *Journal of Forestry.* One of the latter dealt with national forests as the last free hunting grounds of the nation. In the second dozen titles we may see more ornithological notes and articles on game and game refuges, but the future crusader against politics in conservation and misuse of resources is showing up more clearly.

The listed titles from 1920 through most of 1925 are predominantly of short articles on ornithology, hunting and game management, forestry in relation to game management, erosion control, ecological consequences of forest fires, and wilderness values. Included is the one that I regard as his first great paper: "Wilderness as a Form of Land Use," *Journal of Land and Public Utility Economics* 1:398–404 (1925).

The latter was not his first expression of views on wilderness protection. He had published "The Wilderness and Its Place in Forest Recreational Policy," *Journal of Forestry* 19:718–21 (1921), and it is plain from other of his previous writings that he was becoming increasingly aware of the pricelessness of unexploited outdoor areas. The paper on wilderness as a form of land use was more than a statement or plea; it was both solidly informative and a literary contribution. I cannot say how influential it proved to be of itself; but to it, among the others, surely should be credited some of the prominence Aldo attained as an early protagonist of wilderness in national forests. I read in a University of Wisconsin memorial resolution that the U.S. Forest Service subsequently designated a total of 14,000,000 acres as such areas, which are considered to "represent the most visible evidence of his [Aldo's] influence on the American scene." The Leopold writings on wilderness around 1925 are certainly in the historical picture. They still nourish movements for the preservation of wildernesses, not alone in the United States or in North America, but over those parts of the rest of the world where men try to retain irreplaceable natural remnants.

The years 1924–1928, with a transfer to Madison, Wisconsin, to become associate director of the U.S. Forest Products Laboratory, comprised something of an interlude. He wrote relatively little for publication in this period, and what he did write usually dealt with forestry techniques and utilization or with what may be classed as carryover from his life in the Southwest.

Without knowledge of the details behind the selection of Aldo Leopold by the Sporting Arms and Manufacturer's Institute for its game surveys in 1928, one may perceive how he qualified for the job. He was experienced in administration and public contacts, his interests in game and hunting had long been demonstrated, and he had a record of constructive accomplishment in what was then known as game management. Considering the stage of development of management as a field, he was singularly informed. Already, he had contributed to the reversal of the trends toward artificial propagation or tightened legal protection as panaceas for conservation ills; he did not seek complete abandonment of either propagation or protection but rather a judicious balance for them in an incomparably more promising system based upon the ecology of the species concerned. He differentiated between passive conservation and active management and identified management with a desirable type of husbandry of the Earth and its mineral and biotic resources. He was an ecologist and a specialist in his own branch of ecology.

Despite his background, the transition from his old profession to his new one had its abrupt aspects. During the twenty years that he lived as a full-time practitioner of the new profession (and particularly during the first few years), he changed emphasis in several fairly distinct ways.

The changes did not occur in sudden steps. They reflected his accelerating professional growth and the growth of the new field in applied ecology in which he was a "key" worker, the impacts of the man and of the field, of one upon the other.

His game surveys had left him with friends among game administrators, sportsmen, and conservation workers of differing creeds and purposes over the continent. As a man of reason, he kept building on the factual foundations that he had at hand—constantly trying to uncover pertinent researches that had been done or were in progress, encouraging further research, and doing what he could by himself. He did a tremendous amount of reading on conservation history and methods, on the long-established systems of game management of the Old World. Always comparing systems, he tried critically to separate the desirable from the objectionable features of each, to

176

dissociate sound fact from traditional assumption, to understand more of the working of natural mechanisms.

As chairman of a large committee, he did much of the work of preparing the "Report to the American Game Conference on an American Game Policy," *Transactions of the American Game Conference* 17:284–309 (1931), which mentioned the incompatibility of the English and American systems of game management. "Game Methods; the American Way," *American Game* 20:20, 29–31 (1931) was written "to express a personal view of what the policy means in its references to the European practices." In this, the theorem was advanced that "to supply any given proportion of the population with any given amount of game, Europe must raise a denser stand of game per acre, and hence practice a more intensive form of game management than America." Quoting further:

> The recreational value of a head of game is inverse to the artificiality of its origin, and hence in a broad way to the intensiveness of the system of game management which produced it. . . . A game policy should seek . . . between the evident necessity of some management and the aesthetic desideratum of not too much. . . . There is nothing to prevent us from adopting the European technique for producing a game crop, and at the same time rejecting the European customs governing the intensity of the operation and the European system for its harvesting and distribution. The game policy, by and large, proposes just this. . . .

He went on in the same article to challenge

> the ruthless suppression of predators which goes with game management in most European countries. W. T. Hudson has voiced his protest over the disappearance of one predatory species after another, and his resulting contempt for the aesthetic horizon of sportsmen and sportsmanship. . . . American protectionists mortally hate and fear the impending (?) American counterpart of this sacrifice. . . .
>
> I am no prophet. I would point out, however, that stringent predator control is usually unnecessary save in the upper scale of intensive game management . . . we do not need that kind of management. . . . This is not to say that no predator control is needed. It does mean that extensive or low-grade management—enough, let us say, to quintuple our crop—can best be achieved by light, local, seasonal and selective handling of the predator-factor. . . . Is it too much to hope, then, that the group-cooperative wild life enterprise advocated by the game policy may ultimately evolve an

177

American attitude toward predators, based on the new biology, and recognizing the nature-lover and farmer, as well as the sportsman, as joint partners?

In what could almost be called a companion piece—"Game and Wildlife Conservation," *Condor* 34:103-6 (1932)—he drew other important distinctions that the reader could afford to study. Very significant is that between the "schools" of "hardened sportsmen" in this country, exemplified by moderate and extreme factions.

But perhaps nowhere so well as in the concluding paragraphs of the celebrated textbook, *Game Management* (New York: Scribners, 1933, 420-23), does he clarify his reasoning.

The game manager manipulates animals and vegetation to produce a game crop. This, however, is only a superficial indication of his social significance. What he really labors for is to bring about a new attitude toward the land.

The economic determinist regards the land as a food-factory. Though he sings "America" with patriotic gusto, he concedes any factory the right to be as ugly as need be, provided only that it be efficient.

There is another faction which regards economic productivity as an unpleasant necessity, to be kept, like a kitchen, out of sight. Any encroachment on the "parlor" of scenic beauty is quickly resented, sometimes in the name of conservation.

There is a third, and still smaller, minority with which game management by its very essence, is inevitably aligned. It denies that kitchens or factories need be ugly, or farms lifeless, in order to be efficient.

That ugliness which the first faction welcomes as the inevitable concomitant of progress, and which the second regretfully accepts as a necessary compromise, the third rejects as the clumsy result of poor technique, bunglingly applied by a human community which is morally and intellectually unequal to the consequences of its own success. . . .

Herein lies the social significance of game management. It promulgates no doctrine, it simply asks for land and the chance to show that farm, forest, and wild life products can be grown on it, to the mutual advantage of each other, the landowner, and the public. It proposes a motivation—the love of sport—narrow enough actually to get action from human beings as now constituted, but nevertheless capable of expanding with time into that new social concept toward which conservation is groping.

In short, twenty centuries of "progress" have brought the average citizen a vote, a national anthem, a Ford, a bank account, and a high opinion of himself, but not the capacity to live in high density without befouling and denuding his environment, nor a conviction that such capacity, rather than such density, is the true test of whether he is civilized. The practice of game management may be one of the means of developing a culture which will meet this test.

His other writings for this period contain other syntheses of complex subject matter, other pace-setting thought, other excellent composition, and two "heavy" essays: "The Conservation Ethic," *Journal of Forestry* 31:634–43 (1933), and "Conservation Economics," *Journal of Forestry* 32:537–44 (1934)—two of his greatest papers. Among the major changes in professional emphasis to be detected in his publications, 1929–1935, is one from the survey to the intensive method of research and another from game management for shooting to far broader versions of management involving native prairie flowers and songbirds as well as game and game habitats. These changes doubtless may be ascribed partly to changed conditions of employment, notwithstanding which there is plenty of evidence that Aldo's own inclinations led him into them.

In 1935 he studied German game and forest management under a Carl Schurz Travelling Fellowship, publishing his comparisons and conclusions chiefly during the next year: the two-part paper, "Deer and Dauerwald in Germany," *Journal of Forestry* 34:366–75, 460–66 (1936), and semipopular articles in *Bird-Lore* and *American Wildlife.* This trip, by its contrasts, intensified his concern for threatened outdoor values—see, for example, the introduction to the *Bird-Lore* article, "Naturschutz in Germany," in which he depicted the "nostalgia of the German for wildness, as distinguished from mere forests or mere game. . . . We Americans yearn for more deer and more pines, and we shall probably get them. But do we realize that to get them, as the Germans have, at the expense of their wild environment and their wild enemies, is to get very little indeed?"

We have in 1937 the appearance of superbly written short essays, combining ecology and management and a philosophy of esthetics. "Conservationist in Mexico" and "Marshland Elegy," both appearing in *American Forests* (43:118–20, 146, and 472–74), are, I feel, among the first of the fully mature Leopoldian essays of this type. More came out in subsequent years, such as: "Conservation Esthetic," *Bird-Lore* 40:101–9 (1938), "A Biotic View of Land," *Journal of Forestry* 37:727–30 (1939), "Escudilla," *American Forests* 46:539–40 (1940), "Song of the Gavilan," *Journal of Wildlife Management* 4:329–31 (1940), "Cheat Takes Over," the *Land* 1:310–13 (1941), "The Last Stand," *Outdoor America* 7(7):8–9 (1942), "The Flambeau," *American Forests* 49:12–14, 47 (1943), "Wildlife in American Culture," *Journal of Wildlife Management* 7:1–6 (1943), "The Green Lagoons," *American Forests* 51:376–77, 414 (1945), and "The Ecological Conscience," *Bulletin of the Garden Club of America,* (September 1947):46–53. A book of his essays [*Sand County Almanac*], including his revision of some of the above, was published in 1949 by Oxford University Press, New York.

To some degree his later publications reflect changed emphasis, as from advocating monetary or other economic incentives for management to attempting to inculcate appreciation for cultural values. They also indicate a change in emphasis from training of specialists to liberal education as a means to management ends. Aldo worked for long-term "deep-digging" research up to the time of his death, but he saw long before then that the problems of sane land use required more than the attention of professionals. There had to be better motivated, better directed, and better sustained participation by the public if what was good in management was to become a living practice.

As scientist or educator, he was anything but jealous of professional prerogatives. From "Wildlife in American Culture":

> Wildlife research started as a professional priestcraft. The more difficult or laborious problems must remain in professional hands, but there are plenty of problems suitable for all grades of amateurs. . . . Ornithology, mammalogy, and botany, as now known to most amateurs, are but kindergarten games compared with researches in these fields. The real game is decoding the messages written on the face of the land. . . .
>
> Few people can become enthusiastic about research as a sport because the whole structure of biological education is aimed to perpetuate the professional research monopoly. To the amateur is allotted only make-believe voyages of discovery, the chance to verify what professional authority already knows. This is false; the case of Margaret Nice proves what a really enterprising amateur can do. . . .

(He delighted in the ornithological investigations of Mrs. Nice, which in volume and quality surpassed so much of the work of the professionals.)

Long ago he had likened the titles of academic courses to labels on bottles having highly variable contents; and coming from him as a teacher of academic coursework, his paper, "The Role of Wildlife in a Liberal Education" (*Transactions of the North American Wildlife Conference* 7:485–89 [1942]) has quotable paragraphs:

> Liberal education in wildlife is not merely a dilute dosage of technical education. It calls for somewhat different teaching materials and sometimes even different teachers. The objective is to teach the student to see the land, to understand what he sees, and enjoy what he understands. I say land rather than wildlife, because wildlife cannot be understood without understanding the landscape as a whole. Such teaching could well be called land ecology rather than wildlife, and could serve very broad educational purposes.
>
> Perhaps the most important of these purposes is to teach the student how to put the sciences together in order to use them. All the sciences and arts are taught as if they were separate. They are separate only in the classroom. Step out on the campus and they are immediately fused. Land ecology is putting the sciences and arts together for the purpose of understanding our environment. . . .
>
> There is no need to persuade the student of land ecology that machines to dominate the land are useful only while there is a healthy land to use them on, and that land-health is possibly dependent upon land-membership, that is that a flora and fauna too severely simplified or modified might not tick as well as the original. He can see for himself that there is no such thing as good or bad species; a species may get out of hand, but to terminate its membership in the land by human fiat is the last word in anthropomorphic arrogance.

From the paper, "Wildlife in American Culture": "Ecology is now teaching us to search in animal populations for analogies to our own problems. The ability to perceive these, and to appraise them critically, is the woodcraft of the future."

Aldo's personal contacts with students were quite evidently similar to what they had been with me during his game survey years. I learned from the "grapevine" that he exhorted them to write carefully, to revise their manuscripts over and over until organized and smooth, to strive for the maximum simplicity consistent with the subjects written upon. The summer after leaving Wisconsin I brought back to him a medium-length manuscript on the different versions of which I had labored for four months and which I considered ready for the editor; we worked for two days at high pressure, and it took six weeks more of revision to incorporate his suggestions—and that wasn't any too long!

His students, too, could hardly have missed his fairness and what Elton (letter of May 4, 1948) called a "special sort of integrity." My data were always mine, and I have no doubt that his students were assured that their data were theirs and that they could as a matter of course expect a reasonable amount of professorial guidance in handling the same—actually, he was generous with his time to the extent that it frequently meant hardship to him. Nor do I doubt that at least his more mature students respected his intellectual humility.

I remember other things about him from the earlier years. I remember him as a man in the personal crisis of being without income for months during 1932 and 1933 in the worst of the Depression. He took this punishment most creditably, kept up the standard of living of his family as well as circumstances allowed, worked on the manuscript of *Game Management,* and made plans with courage and realism. He was offered desirable positions, including a professorship at a prominent state college, but these would have entailed moving his home from Madison, which he was reluctant to do. Then, the University of Wisconsin established its first Chair of Game Management, later becoming the Department of Wildlife Management.

In appraising Aldo's accomplishments, I would rate the literary essays as the greatest. They reflect him and his thoughts, what McAtee (letter of May 3, 1948 to R. A. McCabe) referred to as "his lucid and stimulating discussions in the conservation field . . . his ever growing power as a writer." In this, his own field of excellence, I don't think that anyone else may be compared with him.

His scientific best is, I think, illustrated by his papers on forest game and land use. These have appeared in widely scattered journals, but the *Journal of Forestry* drew the larger proportion.

His personal inspiration of others is hard to do justice to, whether this was in routine dealings with students or public, or in strategic committee work. In his committee work alone, one must consider not only the dozens of committees of scientific societies and conservation organizations to which he was appointed but also those of extraordinary prestige and importance, such as his chairmanship of the Committee on Wildlife Studies of the National Research Council. Shortly before his death he had been asked by Secretary of State Marshall to be a discussion chairman at the Inter-American Conference on Conservation of Renewable Natural Resources and by Secretary of the Interior Krug to serve on the Advisory Committee on American Participation at the United Nations Scientific Conference on Conservation and Utilization of Resources.

In order to write this memorial as reflectively as I could, I waited until my vacation to do it, to do the writing in a simple log dwelling house near one of the national forests.

A porcupine-girdled pine top may be seen through the front windows, and just out of sight hang the remaining sticks of a goshawk nest that had young in it twelve summers ago. Three species of grouse live along the creek that comes down out of the canyon. If one looks, one may easily find deer and bear sign, and in the hours of darkness, coyotes howl. The air smells richly of pine and sage.

The property on which the log house is situated contributes to the livelihood of people. Along with the sign of native animals is some of horses and cattle. Some land is tilled and some yields hay. Yet the tract surrounding the house is wild and it is intentionally kept so. We are getting rid of the old stumps and other axe-marked wood; our two boys bring it in to burn in the box stove. A large yellow pine with weakened base that we once had to take down to protect the house is an exception: its trunk will be left where it fell, axe and saw cuts and all, ungrudgingly. For a ruffed grouse has accepted it as a drumming log, and in the twilight of evening or early morning, if careful, the family may watch and hear the muffled beating of wings—that "numenon" of northern woodlands. This, I am sure, Aldo would have approved as husbandry.

To the west, the national forest begins. Less than ten miles away is timberline and, below that, are still-occupied retreats of those much reduced prize furbearers, the martens. In the canyons farther below, glacial waters pour over and between boulders, and there are bobcat or lynx tracks in the mud where a game trail leads around a beaver pond. Deep in the forest are said to be a few grizzly bears and even cougars.

The thought of Aldo in connection with this mountain wilderness seems appropriate, though I doubt that he had ever seen it. The love he felt for the out-of-doors and the things that belonged in it was not a matter of geographical boundaries, nor confined to particular settings. In his essay, "Conservation Esthetic," he wrote: "To those devoid of imagination, a blank space on the map is a useless waste; to others, the most valuable part. (Is my share in Alaska worthless to me because I shall never go there? Do I need a road to show me the Arctic prairies, the goose pastures of the Yukon, the Kodiak bear, the sheep meadows behind McKinley?)"

Very probably one so distinguished will be honored posthumously in many ways. There is talk of a memorial fellowship and there may be other movements to perpetuate his name and ideals. Assuredly, these should be encouraged and supported to the extent that they are well-conceived. We must not mock honesty with gestures. I can imagine his gentle scorn at the thought of anything like elaborate statuary in his memory while despoliation and wastage of the land and its biota continue as usual.

For his greatness, as I regard it, lay in the fact that he loved and worked and fought for something greater than himself or any other man. He knew of the peace that outdoor values may give to receptive minds and he wanted those values safeguarded and increased for others as well as for himself. However else it may be designated, his concept of what is worth living in human life has a certain agelessness to it, a solidarity beyond the creative power of any one man. His sense of responsibility and decency is likewise much more than the by-product of any one man's thinking.

Let no one do him the disservice of fostering Leopoldian legends or Leopoldian dogmas. Knowing him as I have, I can say that he would not wish them to arise from his having lived. He would not wish to have imputed to him any qualities or abilities he did not possess. He was only a mortal man, but a highly civilized and intelligent one withal, literate and—most fortunately—articulate in those ways necessary to convert intentions into leadership.

In some respects we might look upon wild beauty, as such, whether in backyard or in remote places, a most fitting memorial to him and to his kind. As his professional colleagues, let us recognize our obligations to a philosophy of living that has goodness in it beyond selfish objectives; and, moreover, that we honor him according to the way we, ourselves, live and lead.

PUBLICATIONS

Books and Journal Articles

1. "The Silence." *Colonial Wig* 2(3):3-12 (1929).
2. "What Can the Wisconsin Farmboy Do to Encourage Quail?" *Wisconsin Arbor and Bird Day Annual* (May 1930):45-49.
3. "Predatory Animals of Southern Wisconsin and Their Value to the Farmer." *Wisconsin Arbor and Bird Day Annual* (May 1930):78-85.
4. "The Pellet Analysis Method of Raptor Food Habits Study." *Condor* 32(6):292-6 (1930).
5. "Corn on Cob Saves Wintering Quail." *American Game* 19(6):9-12 (1930). Also reprinted in *Maryland Conservation* 8(1):13, 26-29 (1931).
6. "Territorial Disputes of Three Pairs of Nesting Marsh Hawks." *Wilson Bulletin* 42(4):237-39 (1930).
7. "Behavior of Bob-whites upon Approach of Marsh Hawks." *Wilson Bulletin* 42(4):294-95 (1930).
8. "Wisconsin Quail Investigation Findings." *Transactions of the American Game Conference* 17:252-53 (1930).
9. "Winter Killing of Barn Owls in Southern Wisconsin." *Wilson Bulletin* 43(1):60 (1931).
10. "Second Winter." (The article deals with winter quail observations.) *American Game* 20(4):56, 60-61 (1931).
11. "The Bob-white's Winter Food." *American Game* 20(5):75-78 (1931).
12. "The Bob-white's Winter Cover." *American Game* 20(6):90-93 (1931)
13. "Quail Winter Food and Cover." *American Game* reprint of numbers 10, 11, and 12 (1932). Also reprinted in *Furs, Fins and Feathers* numbers 114, 115, and 116 (1932-1933).
14. "Technique of Raptor Food Habits Study." *Condor* 34(2):75-85 (1932).
15. "The Man Factor in Game Crops." *American Game* 21(2):26-27 (1932).
16. "Man Management Comes First." *American Game* 21(3):44, 49 (1932).
17. "Wildlife Management: An Integration of Ends in Land Use." *American Game* reprint of 15 and 16 (1932). Also reprinted in *Furs, Fins and Feathers* numbers 113:3, 13, 22-23 (1932).

Bibliography of publications provided by Dr. Kenneth Carlander and Dr. Milton Weller.

18. "The Northern Bob-white: Environmental Factors Influencing Its Status." Ph.D. diss., University of Wisconsin, 1932 (Subject matter of his dissertation was published as separate articles, and the numbers may be considered to represent essentially chapters, listed here in the order of their appearance in the manuscript: 28, 11, 12, 33, 14, 19, 27, 53, 57, 17.)

19. "Food Habits of Southern Wisconsin Raptors." Part I: Owls. *Condor* 34(4):176–86 (1932).

20. "Great Horned Owls Dying in the Wild from Disease." *Wilson Bulletin* 44(3):180 (1932).

21. "An Encounter between a Cooper's Hawk and a Horned Owl." *Wilson Bulletin* 44(3):189 (1932).

22. "Iowa Researching." *American Game* 21(5):74, 80 (1932).

23. "Iowa's Wildlife Research Program." (Revision of No. 22). *Transactions of American Game Conference* 19:346–50 (1932).

24. "Suggestions as to Nesting Studies of Iowa Game Birds." *Iowa Bird Life* 2(4):46–48 (1932).

25. "Studies on the Behavior of the Great Horned Owl." *Wilson Bulletin* 44(4):212–20 (1932).

26. "Mobility of the Northern Bob-white as Indicated by Banding Returns." *Bird Banding* 4(1):1–7 (1933).

27. "Food Habits of Southern Wisconsin Raptors." Part II: Hawks. *Condor* 35(1):19–29 (1933).

28. "The Wintering of the Wisconsin Bob-white." *Transactions of the Wisconsin Academy of Science, Arts and Letters* 28:1–35 (1933).

29. "The Management of the Bob-white Quail in Iowa." *Iowa Agricultural Extension Bulletin* 186. 15 pp. 1933.

30. "Another Winter's Quail Study." *American Game* 22(3):39, 44–45 (1933).

31. "The Long-eared Owl as a Ratter." *Condor* 35(4):163 (1933).

32. "Summer Bob-white Observations in a City Backyard." *Iowa Bird Life* 3(3):36–37 (1933).

33. "The Nesting and the Life Equation of the Wisconsin Bob-white." *Wilson Bulletin* 45(3):122–32 (1933).

34. (and Logan J. Bennett). "Lost Legions." (An article dealing with game bird losses from crippling incidental to hunting.) *Outdoor Life* 72(3):18–19, 56 (1933).

35. (and Logan J. Bennett). "Midwest Duck Breeding Grounds." *Minnesota Conservation* 4:8, 18–20 (1933).

36. "Bob-white Winter Survival in an Area Heavily Populated with Grey Foxes." *Iowa State College Journal of Science* 8(1):127–33 (1933).

37. "Report on Precarious Wild Fowl Conditions." *Outdoor Life* 72(5):25–26 (1933).

38. "Second Broods in the Mallard Duck." *Auk* 51(1):78–80 (1934).

39. (and Logan J. Bennett). "Iowa Duck Studies." *Transactions of American Game Conference* 20:249–57 (1934).

40. "A Late Iowa Record for an American Bittern." *Wilson Bulletin* 46(1):62–63 (1934).

41. "Vulnerability of Bob-white Populations to Predation." *Ecology* 15(2):110–27 (1934).
42. "Predatory Animals, Birds, and Snakes." Pp. 51–60 in *Furs, Fins and Feathers*. Des Moines, Iowa: Meredith, 1934. 64 pp.
43. "Wildlife Research as a Profession." *Scientific Monthly* 38(6):554–60 (1934).
44. "Quail Shooting Quota Fixed by Study of Winter Survival." *Iowa Fish and Game Guide* 1(2):4 (1934).
45. "Carrying Capacity Controls Quail Population Survival." *Iowa Fish and Game Guide* 1(3):3–4 (1934).
46. "Predators and the Northern Bob-white." *American Forests* 41(1):7–10, 46 (1935).
47. "Wintering of Field-living Norway Rats in South-central Wisconsin." *Ecology* 16(1):122–23 (1935).
48. "What Counts in Northern Bob-white Management." *Transactions of American Game Conference* 21:370–76 (1935). Also reprinted p. 207 in *Field Circular* 6, Soil Conservation Service Region 7, 1937.
49. "The Significance of Food Habits Research in Wildlife Management." *Science* 81(2103):378–79 (1935). Reprinted, pp. 727–28 in *Value of Research into the Food Habits of Wildlife*, an excerpt from "Hearing before the Subcommittee of House Committee on Appropriations, in Charge of the Agricultural Department Appropriation Bill for 1936," 717–37 (1935).
50. "Winter-killing of Mourning Doves in Central Iowa." *Wilson Bulletin* 47(2):159–60 (1935).
51. "The 1934 Drought and Southern Iowa Bobwhite." *Iowa Bird Life* 5(2):18–21 (1935).
52. (and Logan J. Bennett). "Food Habits of Burrowing Owls in Northwestern Iowa." *Wilson Bulletin* 47(2):125–28 (1935).
53. "Food Habits of Mid-west Foxes." *Journal of Mammalogy* 16(3):192–200 (1935).
54. (and F. N. Hamerstrom, Jr.). "Bob-white Winter Survival on Experimentally Shot and Unshot Areas." *Iowa State College Journal of Science* 9(4):625–39 (1935).
55. "Over-populations and Predation: A Research Field of Singular Promise." *Condor* 37(5):230–32 (1935).
56. "Sex and Resistance of Bob-whites and Ring-necked Pheasants to Starvation." *Auk* 53(1):78–79 (1936).
57. "Notes on Food Habits of Southern Wisconsin House Cats." *Journal of Mammalogy* 17(1):64–65 (1936).
58. "Differences in Nutritive Values of Winter Game Foods." *Proceedings of the North American Wildlife Conference* 1:356–360 (1936). Also reprinted in *Minnesota Conservation* 51:29–32 (1937).
59. "The Winter of 1934–35 and Iowa Bob-whites." *American Midland Naturalist* 17(2):554–68 (1936).
60. "Shooting and Bob-white Populations." *Game Breeder and Sportsman* 40(4):79, 91–93 (1936).
61. (and W. E. Albert, Jr.). "Banding Studies of Semidomesticated

Mallard Ducks." *Bird Banding* 7(2):69–73 (1936).
62. "Iowa Experiments with Quail." *Outdoor American N. S.* 1(7):4–5, 16 (1936).
63. (and F. N. Hamerstrom, Jr.). "The Northern Bob-white's Winter Territory." *Iowa Agricultural Experiment Station Research Bulletin* 201:301–443 (1936).
64. "Bone Healing in Young Marsh Hawks." *Auk* 53(3)326–27 (1936).
65. "Winter-killing of Flickers in Central Iowa." *Auk* 53(3):334–35 (1936).
66. "Sex Ratio and Size Variation in South Dakota Mink." *Journal of Mammalogy* 17(3):287 (1936).
67. "Re-stocking Quail in Our Northern States." *Minnesota Conservation* 39:10–11, 15 (1936).
68. (and W. J. Breckenridge). "Food Habits of Marsh Hawks in the Glaciated Prairie Region of North-central United States." *American Midland Naturalist* 17(5):831–48 (1936).
69. "Food Habits of a Weasel Family." *Journal of Mammalogy* 17(4):406–7 (1936).
70. "Food Habits of Iowa Red Foxes during a Drought Summer." *Ecology* 18(1):53–60 (1937).
71. "Food Habits of the Red Fox in Iowa." *American Wildlife* 26(1):5–6, 13 (1937).
72. "Winter Carrying Capacity of Marginal Ruffed Grouse Environment in North-central United States." *Canadian Field Naturalist* 51(3):31–34 (1937).
73. "Recent Predator Studies." *Pennsylvania Game News* 7(12):14, 30 (1937).
74. "Management of the Red Fox in Iowa." *American Wildlife* 26(2):24, 30–31 (1937).
75. "Habitat Requirements of Stream-dwelling Muskrats." *Transactions of the North American Wildlife Conference* 2:411–16 (1937).
76. "Summer Food Habits of the Badger in Northwestern Iowa." *Journal of Mammalogy* 18(2):213–16 (1937).
77. (and R. M. Berry). "Tagging Studies of Red Foxes." *Journal of Mammalogy* 18(2):203–5 (1937).
78. "Summer Food Habits of the Short-eared Owl in Northwestern Iowa." *Wilson Bulletin* 49(2):121 (1937).
79. (and F. N. Hamerstrom, Jr.). "The Evaluation of Nesting Losses and Juvenile Mortality of the Ring-necked Pheasant." *Journal of Wildlife Management* 1(1–2):3–20 (1937).
80. "The Breeding Season of the Muskrat in Northeast Iowa." *Journal of Mammalogy* 18(3):333–37 (1937).
81. "Preface to Teaching Unit 5: Owls." 4 pp. *Emergency Conservation Communication Publication* 67 (1937).
82. "A Wood Duck Marsh in Northwestern Iowa." *Auk* 54(4):533–34 (1937).
83. "Emergency Values of Some Winter Pheasant Foods." *Transac-*

tions of the Wisconsin Academy of Science, Arts and Letters 30:57–68 (1937).

84. (and Carolyn Storm Errington). "Experimental Tagging of Young Muskrats for Purposes of Study." *Journal of Wildlife Management* 1(3–4):49–61 (1937).
85. "What Is the Meaning of Predation?" *Annual Report of Smithsonian Institution.* 1936:243–52 (1937) Also reprinted in condensed form in *Park Service Bulletin* 7(11), suppl. 1–6 (1937).
86. "Drowning as a Cause of Mortality in Muskrats." *Journal of Mammalogy* 18(4):497–500 (1937).
87. (and Malcolm McDonald)."Conclusions as to the Food Habits of the Barred Owl in Iowa." *Iowa Bird Life* 7(4):47–49 (1937).
88. "Quality of Winter Pheasant Foods." *Game Breeder and Sportsman* 41(11):202–3 (1937).
89. "No Quarter." (Winter Mortality of the Muskrat Used as a Literary Subject.) *Bird Lore* 40(1):5–6 (1938).
90. "Experimental Evidence on the Eating of Bob-white Eggs by Small *Sciuridae.*" *Journal of Mammalogy* 19(1):107–8 (1938).
91. (and F. N. Hamerstrom, Jr.). "Observations on the Effect of Spring Drought on Reproduction in the Hungarian Partridge." *Condor* 40(2):115–19 (1938).
92. "The Marsh Hawk and Its Hunting." *Bird Lore* 40(2):115–19 (1938).
93. "Modern Science and Predation." (Reprint of No. 46, condensed.) *Angler and Hunter* 3(5):11,14 (1938).
94. "The Decline of a Mink Population." *Journal of Mammalogy* 19(2):250–51 (1938).
95. (and W. J. Breckenridge). "Food Habits of Buteo Hawks in North-central United States." *Wilson Bulletin* 50(2):113–21 (1938).
96. "Observations on Muskrat Damage to Corn and Other Crops in Central Iowa." *Journal of Agricultural Research* 57(6):415–21 (1938).
97. (Breckenridge, W. J. and). "Food Habits of Small Falcons in North-central States." *Auk* 55(4):668–70 (1938).
98. "The Great Horned Owl as an Indicator of Vulnerability in Prey Populations." *Journal of Wildlife Management* 2(4):190–205 (1938).
99. (and H. L. Stoddard). "Modifications in Predation Theory Suggested by Ecological Studies of the Bob-white Quail." *Transactions of the North American Wildlife Conference* 3:736–40 (1938).
100. "More on Predation." *Angler and Hunter* 3(9–10):15 (1938).
101. "The Comparative Ability of the Bob-white and the Ring-necked Pheasant to Withstand Cold and Hunger." *Wilson Bulletin* 51(1):22–37 (1939).
102. "Foods of the Bob-white in Wisconsin." *Auk* 56(2):170–73 (1939).
103. "Reactions of Muskrat Populations to Drought." *Ecology* 20(2):168–86 (1939).

104. "Publication Standards in Wildlife Management." *Journal of Wildlife Management* 3(2):162–65 (1939).
105. "Suggestions for Appraising Effects of Predation on Local Areas Managed for Bob-white." *Transactions of the North American Wildlife Conference* 4:422–25 (1939).
106. "Observations on Young Muskrats in Iowa." *Journal of Mammalogy* 20(4):465–78 (1939).
107. "Natural Restocking of Muskrat-vacant Habitats." *Journal of Wildlife Management* 4(2):173–85 (1940).
108. (Frances Hamerstrom and F. N. Hamerstrom, Jr.). "The Great Horned Owl and Its Prey in North-central United States." *Iowa Agricultural Experiment Station Research Bulletin* 277:757–850 (1940).
109. "On the Social Potentialities of Wildlife Management." (Editorial) *Journal Wildlife Management* 4(4):451–52 (1940).
110. "Muskrats in the Corn." *Farm Science Reporter* 1(4):14–16 (1940).
111. "Versatility in Feeding and Population Maintenance of the Muskrat." *Journal of Wildlife Management* 5(1):68–89 (1941).
112. "An Eight-winter Study of Central Iowa Bob-whites." *Wilson Bulletin* 53(2):85–102 (1941).
113. "Objectives in Civil Service." *Journal of Wildlife Management* 5(3):346–49 (1941).
114. "Notes on Winter-killing of Central Iowa Bob-whites." *Iowa Bird Life* 11(3):46–49 (1941).
115. "On the Analysis of Productivity in Populations of Higher Vertebrates." *Journal of Wildlife Management* 6(2):165–81 (1942).
116. "Observations on a Fungus Skin Disease of Iowa Muskrats." *American Journal of Veterinary Research* 3(7):195–201 (1942).
117. "Some Commonly Asked Questions about Muskrats." *Iowa Conservation* 1(7):5–6 (1942).
118. "The 1942 Floods and Central Iowa Muskrats." *Iowa Conservation* 2:27 (1943).
119. "An Analysis of Mink Predation upon Muskrats in North-central United States." *Iowa Agricultural Experiment Station Research Bulletin* 320:797–924 (1943).
120. "Mink Predation upon Muskrats." *Iowa Conservation* 2(9):70, 72 (1943).
121. "Pigments and Public: Or When Should the Muskrat Season Open?" *Iowa Conservation* 2(12):95–96 (1943).
122. "To Babes Really Lost in the Woods." *Canadian Field Naturalist* 58(2):52–54 (1944).
123. "Additional Studies on Tagged Young Muskrats." *Journal of Wildlife Management* 8(3):300–6 (1944).
124. "Iowa Muskrat Situation in the Fall of 1944." *Iowa Conservation* 3(10):80 (1944).
125. (Allen, A. A., _____, J. J. Hickey, J. A. Munro, and D. Stoner). "Report of the A.O.U. Committee on Bird Protection for 1943." *Auk* 61(4):622–35 (1944).
126. "Some Contributions of a Fifteen-year Local Study of the North-

ern Bob-white to a Knowledge of Population Phenomena." *Ecological Monographs* 15(1):1–34 (1945).

127. (and Thomas G. Scott). "Reduction in Productivity of Muskrat Pelts on an Iowa Marsh through Depredations of Red Foxes." *Journal of Agricultural Research* 71(4):137–48 (1945).

128. "Fur Refuge Experiments Pay Out." *Iowa Conservation* 4(10):175–76 (1945).

129. "The Pheasant in the Northern Prairie States," 190–202. In *The Ring-Necked Pheasant,* ed. W. L. McAtee. Washington, D.C.: American Wildlife Institute, 1945, xi + 320.

130. "Iowa Muskrats in 1945." *Iowa Conservation* 4(11):177, 184 (1945).

131. _____ (Jean M. Linsdale, and J. A. Munro). "Report of the A.O.U. Committee on Bird Protection for 1944." *Auk* 62(4):613–19 (1945).

132. "Predation and Vertebrate Populations." (First part.) *Quarterly Review of Biology* 21(2):144–77 (1946).

133. "Predation and Vertebrate Populations." (Conclusion.) *Quarterly Review of Biology* 21(3):221–45 (1946).

134. "A Question of Values." *Journal of Wildlife Management* 11(3):267–72 (1947). Also reprinted in *Wisconsin Conservation Bulletin* 12(12):19–22 (1947); in *Outdoor Unlimited* (Feb. 1948); in *Genesee Sportsman* 2(4):6–10 (1948); and 481–89 in Pearl Hogrefe's *The Process of Creative Writing*. Rev. ed. New York: Harper, 1956.

135. "Environmental Control for Increasing Muskrat Production." *Transactions of the North American Wildlife Conference* 13:596–607 (1948).

136. _____ (Jean M. Linsdale, John W. Aldrich, Ian MacTaggart Cowan, Philip A. DuMont, and S. Charles Kendeigh). "Report of the A.O.U. Committee on Bird Protection for 1947." *Auk* 65(1):117–24 (1948).

137. "In Appreciation of Aldo Leopold." *Journal of Wildlife Management* 12(4):341–50 (1948).

138. "Concerning Fluctuations in Populations of the Prolific and Widely Distributed Muskrat." *American Naturalist* 85(824):273–92 (1951).

139. "The Mathematical Muskrat." *Iowa Conservation* 11(6):41, 47, and 11(7):51 (1952).

140. "Et spørsmål om verdier." (Translation into Norwegian and reprinting of 132). *Viltet* 1952:103–10 (1952).

141. "A Closer Look at the Killers." *Audubon Magazine* 55(1):12–15, 22–23 (1953). Also reprinted in *Virginia Wildlife* 14(8):4–7, 22 (1953).

142. "Of a Lynx and a White Cedar Swamp." *Conservation Volunteer* 16(92):16–17 (1953). Also reprinted in *Bowhunter* 7(12):13 (1953).

143. "On Scandinavian Literature in Wildlife Management and Ecology." *Journal of Wildlife Management* 17(4):393–97 (1953).

144. "On the Hazards of Overemphasizing Numerical Fluctuations in

191

Studies of 'Cyclic' Phenomena in Muskrat Populations." (A contribution to a Symposium on Cycles in Animal Populations.) *Journal of Wildlife Management* 18(1):66–90 (1954).

145. "On the Conservation of the Lynx in Scandinavia." *Journal of Mammalogy* 35(2):254–55 (1954).

146. "The 'Big Boss' of the Woods." *Audubon Magazine* 56(3):124–27 (1954).

147. "The Special Responsiveness of Minks to Epizootics in Muskrat Populations." *Ecological Monographs* 24(4):377–93 (1954).

148. "Our Little Wild Dogs—the Foxes." *Audubon Magazine* 57(1):14–17, 27 (1955).

149. "Factors Limiting Higher Vertebrate Populations." *Science* 124(3216):304–7 (1956).

150. "Minken och bisamrattån" ("The Mink and the Muskrat"). Svensk Jakt 94(11):386–89 (1956).

151. "Toward a Better Understanding of Animal Life." *American Biology Teacher* 19(4):103–6 (1957).

152. "Of Population Cycles and Unknowns." *Cold Spring Harbor Symposia on Quantitative Biology* 22:287–300 (1957).

153. "Summer in a Prairie Marsh." (A chapter prepublished from 154.) *Audubon Magazine* 59(4):154–57, 176–77 (1957).

154. *Of Men and Marshes.* New York: Macmillan, 1957, ix + 150.

155. "Of Marshes and Spring" (a chapter from 154 for an anthology for freshman English), 139–150. *Approaches to Prose*, ed. Caroline Schrodes and Justine Van Gundy. New York: Macmillan, 1959, ix + 648.

156. "Rovdjuren och balansen i naturen" ("Predators and the Balance of Nature"). *Djurens Värld* 3:6–8 and 4:14–18 (1959).

157. (with F. W. Brasestrup). "Rovdyrene og deres virkninger—nogle synspunkter ("Predatory Animals and Their Effects—Some Viewpoints"). *Naturens Verden* (April):71–81 (1960).

158. "Wetland Saga." *Natural History* 69(3):8–15 (1960).

159. "The Wonder of an Iowa Marsh." *Iowan* 8(7):41–45 (1960).

160. "Ett år i Sverige" ("A Year in Sweden"). *Sveriges Naturs Årsbok*:170–83 (1961).

161. "An Iowa Boyhood." (A memorial to Arthur Karr Gilkey.) *Iowan* 9(4):4–5, 43–44 (1961).

162. "An American Visitor's Impressions of Scandinavian Waterfowl Problems." *Journal of Wildlife Management* 25(2):109–30 (1961).

163. "Canadian North," 113–26. In *Discovery: Great Moments in the Lives of Outstanding Naturalists*, ed. John K. Terres. Philadelphia: J. P. Lippincott, 1961, xiii + 338.

164. "Of Marshes and Fall" (reprint of chapter from 154 for an anthology), 310–19. In *The American Year: Nature Across America through the Four Seasons, as Observed by the Great Writers and Naturalists of the Past and Present*, ed. Henry Hill Collins, Jr. New York: G. P. Putnam, 1961, xxix + 447.

165. Muskrats and Marsh Management. Harrisburg, Pa.: Stackpole,

and The Wildlife Management Institute, Washington, D.C., 1961, 183.
166. (and David W. Waller). "The Bounty System in Iowa." *Proceedings of the Iowa Academy of Science* 68:301-13 (1961).
167. "Marshland Saga." *Michigan Conservation* 31(1):8-13 (1962).
168. "Of Man and the Lower Animals." *Yale Review* 51(3):370-83 (1962).
169. "Wilderness Islands of the North." *Natural History* 71(5):8-17 (1962).
170. "Disease Cycles in Nature—Epizootiology of a Disease in Muskrats," 7-25. In *The Problems of Laboratory Animal Disease,* ed. R. J. C. Harris. London and New York: Academic Press, 1962.
171. _____ (Roger J. Siglin and Robert C. Clark). "The Decline of a Muskrat Population." *Journal of Wildlife Management* 27(1): 1-8 (1963).
172. "The Pricelessness of Untampered Nature." *Journal of Wildlife Management* 27(2):313-20 (1963).
173. "The Phenomenon of Predation." *American Scientist* 51(2):180-92 (1963).
174. *Muskrat Populations.* Ames: Iowa State Univ. Press, 1963, 665.
175. "An Iowa Marsh." In *The Bird Watcher's America,* ed. O. S. Pettingill. New York: McGraw-Hill, 1965
176. *Of Predation and Life.* Ames: Iowa State Univ. Press, 1967, xiii + 277.
177. "Of Man and Maturity." *Atlantic Naturalist* 23(4):195-203 (1968).
178. "Of Wilderness and Wolves." *Living Wilderness* 33(107):3-7 (1969), and 34(112):49-51 (1970-1971).
179. *The Red Gods Call.* Ames: Iowa State Univ. Press, 1973, ix + 171.

Reviews

R1. *The Hawks of North America.* (John B. May.) *Bird Lore* 37(4):283 (1935).
R2. *Studies in the Life History of the Song Sparrow.* (Margaret Morse Nice.) *Wilson Bulletin* 49(4):308 (1937).
R3. *Life Histories of North American Birds of Prey. Part II* (Arthur Cleveland Bent.) *Bird Lore* 40(6):447-48 (1938).
R4. *Bob-white Populations as Affected by Woodland Management in Eastern Texas.* (Daniel W. Lay.) *Wilson Bulletin* 53(1):21 (1941).
R5. *Wildlife Conservation.* (Ira N. Gabrielson.) *Ecology* 22(3):347-48 (1941).
R6. *Nesting Birds and the Vegetation Substrate.* (William J. Beecher.) *Ecology* 23(4):493-94 (1942).
R7. *The Wolves of North America.* (Stanley P. Young and Edward A.

Goldman.) *Ecology* 26(1):108 (1945).

R8. *Mammals of Nevada.* (E. Raymond Hall.) *Ecology* 28(1):82–83 (1947).

R9. *Fox Squirrels and Gray Squirrels in Illinois.* (Louis G. Brown and Lee E. Yeager.) *Quarterly Review of Biology* 22(2):145 (1947).

R10. *The General Ecological Characteristics of the Outbreak Areas and Outbreak Years of the Australian Plague Locust* (Chortoicetes terminifera *Walk.*) (K. H. L. Key) *Quarterly Review of Biology* 22(3):213 (1947).

R11. *An Account of Experiments Undertaken to Determine the Natural Population Density of the Sheep Blowfly,* Lucilia cuprina *Wied.* (Darcy Gilmour, D. F. Waterhouse, and G. A. McIntyre.) *Quarterly Review of Biology* 22(3):214 (1947).

R12. *The California Ground Squirrel: A Record of Observations Made on the Hastings Natural History Reservation.* (Jean M. Linsdale.) *Quarterly Review of Biology* 22(3):215–16 (1947).

R13. *Querschnitt durch eine mehrjährige Nahrungskontrolle einiger Uhupaare.* (Rob. März.) *Bird Banding* 21(3):122 (1950).

R14. *A Study of Small Mammal Populations in Northern Michigan.* (Richard H. Manville.) *Quarterly Review of Biology* 25(3):324–25 (1950).

R15. *The Muskrat in the Louisiana Coastal Marshes: A Study of the Ecological, Geological, Biological, Tidal, and Climatic Factors Governing the Production and Management of the Muskrat Industry in Louisiana.* (Ted O'Neil.) *Journal of Mammalogy* 32(1):127–28 (1951).

R16. *Dispersal, Amount of Inbreeding, and Longevity in a Local Population of Prairie Deer Mice on the George Reserve, Southern Michigan.* (Walter E. Howard.) *Quarterly Review of Biology* 26(1):73–74 (1951).

R17. *Ecological Animal Geography.* (W. C. Allee and Karl P. Schmidt.) *Science* 115(2984):273–74 (1952).

R18. *Deer and Their Management in the Deer Parks of Great Britain and Ireland.* (G. Kenneth Whitehead.) *Quarterly Review of Biology* 27(2):221 (1952).

R19 *Practice of Wildlife Conservation.* (Leonard W. Wing.) *Quarterly Review of Biology* 27(3):323 (1952).

R20. *Methodology and Techniques for the Study of Animal Societies.* (Roy Waldo Miner, ed. et al.) *Quarterly Review of Biology* 27(4):433 (1952).

R21. *Natural Communities.* (Lee R. Dice.) *Science* 117(3028):43 (1953).

R22. *Introduced Mammals of New Zealand: An Ecological and Economic Survey.* (K. A. Wodzicki.) *Quarterly Review of Biology* 28(1):50 (1953).

R23. *The North American Buffalo: A Critical Study of the Species in Its Wild State.* (Frank Gilbert Roe.) *Quarterly Review of Biology* 28(1):51 (1953).

R24. *The Mammals of Minnesota.* (Harvey L. Gunderson and James R. Beer.) *Scientific Monthly* 78(2):127 (1954).
R25. *The Monkey Book.* (Ernest P. Walker.) *Scientific Monthly* 79(6):414 (1954).
R26. *The Distribution and Abundance of Animals.* (H. G. Andrewartha and L. C. Birch.) *Science* 121(3142):389–90 (1955).
R27. *Principles of General Ecology.* (Angus M. Woodbury.) *Quarterly Review of Biology* 30(1):57 (1955).
R28. *Wildlife in Alaska.* (A. Starker Leopold and F. Fraser Darling.) *Quarterly Review of Biology* 30(1):59 (1955).
R29. *Précis d'écologie animale.* (F. S. Bodenheimer.) *Quarterly Review of Biology* 31(1):43 (1956).
R30. *Red Foxes and a Declining Prey Population.* (Thomas G. Scott and Willard D. Klimstra.) *Quarterly Review of Biology* 31(1):44 (1956).
R31. *Fiskarma i Färg.* (Kai Curry-Lindahl.) *Journal of Wildlife Management* 22(3):330 (1958).
R32. *Die Bisamratte: Ihre Lebensgewohnheiten, Vetbreitung, Bekämpfung und wirtschaftliche bedeutung.* (Max Hoffmann.) *Journal of Mammalogy* 40:624 (1959).
R33. *Biologishe Studien am Alpensegler.* (Hans Arn-Wille.) *Auk* 78:445–46 (1961).
R34. *Alexander Wilson: Naturalist and Pioneer.* (Robert Cantwell.) *Iowa Bird Life* 31:92 (1961).
R35. *Stories from Under the Sky.* (John Madson.) *Journal of Wildlife Management* 26(4):417–18 (1962).

Some Biographical Citations

Bodenheimer, F. A. *Animal Ecology To-day.* The Hague, Netherlands: W. Junk, 1958, 276. Dedicated to Dr. Paul L. Errington and three other "great pioneers of animal ecology." Particular reference to Dr. Errington's contribution on 8, 11, 105–11.
Ratcliffe, F. N. "*Section D: Zoology. Presidential Address: Factors Involved in the Regulation of Mammal and Bird Populations.*" *Australian Journal of Science* 21(5a):79–87 (1958). Includes a tribute to Paul Errington and his contributions.
"A New Elite of American Naturalists: Heirs of a Great Tradition." *Life Magazine* 51(25):103–10 (Dec. 1961). Photograph and citation of Dr. Paul Errington as one of ten outstanding naturalists.
The Aldo Leopold Award (to Dr. P. L. Errington), 315–16, In "Wildlife Society Reports for 1961-62." *Journal of Wildlife Management* 26(3):306–20 (1962).
"Paul L. Errington: The Man of the Marshes." (By David Hoopes.) *Scientist* (an Iowa State University student publication) 16(3):6–7 (Nov. 1962).
"In Memoriam. Paul L. Errington, 1902–1962." *Wisconsin Academic Review* 10(2):94 (1963).

PUBLICATIONS

"Obituary. Paul L. Errington, 1902–1962." (By Thomas G. Scott)
Journal of Wildlife Management 27(2):321–24 (1963).
"Resolution of Respect. Paul L. Errington, 1902–1962." (By Milton W.
Weller.) *Bulletin of the Ecology Society of America* 44(2):55–58
(1963).
"In Memoriam. Paul Lester Errington, 1902–1962." (By K. D.
Carlander) *Proceedings of the Iowa Academy of Science* 70:
(1964).
"In Memoriam. Paul Lester Errington." (By A. W. Schorger.) *Auk*
(1964).

196